Daniella Preleshnik, a 14-year-old Jewish girl, left her home in Poland one day in 1939 and never returned. Her subsequent life was spent in the ghetto, in labour camps and in the 'House of Dolls', one of the houses of prostitution set up by the Nazis for their armed forces. Based on an authentic diary, *House of Dolls* with its hideous revelations and characters such as Daniella's blonde Aryan torturess, here called Elsa, is the most appalling and famous confession on record of the terror that finally broke the millions of men and women who were savaged by Europe's great catastrophe.

By the same author

Shivitti

KA-TZETNIK 135633

House of Dolls

Grafton Books

A Division of HarperCollins*Publishers*

GraftonBooks
A Division of HarperCollins*Publishers*
77–85 Fulham Palace Road,
Hammersmith, London W6 8JB

Published by GraftonBooks 1956
Reprinted fifty times
9 8 7 6 5 4 3 2

First published in Great Britain by
Frederick Muller Ltd 1956

ISBN 0-586-02545-6

Printed in Great Britain by
HarperCollinsManufacturing Glasgow

Set in Plantin

Hebrew edition – *Dvir*; Danish – *Steen Hasselbalch*;
Swedish – *Forum AB*; Japanese – *Kawade Shobo*;
Italian – *Mondadori Editore*; Yiddish – *Union Central and Peretz*;
Spanish – *Argentina Editorial*; French – *Gallimard NRF*;
Bulgarian – *Fatherland Front*; Czech – *Nase Vosjko*;
German – *Edition GP*.

To Nike
without whom this book would not
have been written
                    (S.D'M.A.)

Translated from the Hebrew
by Moshe M. Kohn

K.Z. (German-pronounced Ka-tzet) are the initials of Kozentration Zenter (concentration camp). Every K.Z.-inmate was nicknamed "Ka-tzetnik Number . . ." – the personal number branded into the flesh of the left arm. The writer of *House of Dolls* was Ka-tzetnik 135633.

1

"DANIELLA," he called softly to her, "why didn't you come for a warm snack last night? We waited for you."

The voice came from just behind her. She knew immediately it was Vevke standing there. No one else pronounced the "l" in her name so hard yet with such fatherly tenderness.

She went on ripping the seam of the striped trousers.

"Thanks, Vevke," she answered, without turning to face him, "but I'm not hungry. Really."

"You won't make us any poorer," he continued, whispering over her shoulder. "An eighth mouth is no strain on a pot that feeds seven. Don't be stubborn."

Schultze stood on the threshold of the rag room, gripping his cane point up, like a Prussian officer saluting with his sword. Vevke stooped quickly to scoop up a pile of rags, and carried it out with a swing on his powerful, upraised forearms. The women followed him with mute, furtive side glances as he swung into the cutting room and deposited his load on one of the high cutting-tables.

There are moments when the pile of worn clothing in the centre of the rag room bestirs itself suddenly like a volcano and sends a pervasive fear throughout the large room. The women, huddled at their benches around the clothes heap, are suddenly still. Their hands manipulate the knives like priestesses readying a ram for offer to a hungry god. The heap fumes in fearful wrath—a wrath, it seems, that will never be quenched. But for the most part, the heap is still —as only a heap of ragged old clothes can be still—while the mouths of the women around it pour out a steady stream of prattle.

Over the rag room is the machine room, where hundreds of sewing machines whir on without stop. Some of the operators, anxious to fill their quotas, work so intently that

7

the treadles of their machines clatter on the floor, and below, in the rag room, the ceiling rumbles like muffled thunderclaps rolling across the sky. The din never lets up. The people have become used to it, like inhabitants of a fishing village to the roar of the surf.

Daniella draws a garment from the clothes heap—men's raincoats are easiest to rip. A long seam runs down the back of this type of coat, and the knife flows right through the seam unhindered—leaving time to daydream. The work is easy. The pockets aren't attached with outside seams, and there is no fear that the sharp cobbler's knife will slip and cut the material.

But the trouble is, you're not allowed to sample through the pile; everyone has to take what comes, off the top. It's all a matter of luck. Everything here is a matter of luck; every so often a gold coin is found hidden, of all places, in the collar of a small child's coat.

No one knows from where the large vans bring the piles of clothing to the shoe factory warehouses day after day. No one knows where the people are who wore these piles of clothes, and no one pursues this thought to its logical conclusion: where were these people taken to—naked, unclothed? But everyone knows that near Breslau there is a vast camp where they do nothing but sift these very clothes for hidden valuables that might be sewn into them.

There, at Camp Breslau, the clothes are sorted: the newer and better ones are shipped to Germany, the shabbier ones are bought by Himmler's Labour Commissioner for the shoe factory recently opened in the ghetto. Here they are ripped, and uppers are cut from them for the wooden shoes the Gestapo buys by the hundreds of thousands—for the Gestapo only knows what purpose.

Now even if Daniella were to pick through the clothes heap, and select the best garment to work on, none of the women would dare say a word. They all know that this blonde miss is looked after by Vevke, technical supervisor of the shoe factory. But Daniella wouldn't do it; she can't. Were she merely to reach into the heap to pick one of the easier pieces, all eyes would immediately be upon her, sullenly watching. She can't stand the stares of these women. All day long they scan what is going on all around them. They cut their fingers on the sharp cobblers' knives, but this doesn't teach them to stop spying on one another. Each is afraid her neighbour might uncover a treasure among the seams. Their eyes are tense, nervous; their hearts pound; and their bird-step glances skip about—left and right, from hands to hands.

No one knows if there is anything hidden in the seams of the garment some hands have just pulled from the heap. All draw from the same clothes heap. Every jacket has a collar and all the trousers have the same hidden seams. Everyone knows the garments have been carefully searched at Camp Breslau. Nevertheless, the eyes never relax. They might catch a glimpse of a gold coin flashing out of a ripped seam into a stranger's hand; or detect some hands unrolling a long, green strip of paper—an American "noodle"—from a hanger loop. After all, the examiners at Camp Breslau are only human.

To the right is the cutting room; to the left the cobblers'. The foremen and section heads scramble frantically about. The work rages on. Schultze, the chief German supervisor, slithers along the walls of the workrooms with his cane. Vevke moves from workbench to workbench, ostensibly bringing to each bench fresh material to be worked. But Vevke knows his workers. He knows near whom to pause so he will be on hand for a quick rescue job—to save a shoe from ruination by a new-sprung cobbler, and the "cobbler" from deportation to Auschwitz; for to Schultze a spoiled shoe is "wilful sabotage."

. . . He's a strange one, Vevke, thinks Daniella. For him there are still seven. *"An eighth mouth is no strain on a pot that feeds seven . . ."* Since the disaster with Tedek, she hasn't been able to show her face in Vevke's hovel. And she'll never go there again. Actually, Vevke should hate her; his whole family should hate her. Tedek was the favourite son, the family darling. They all used to glory in him so: Tedek. Doesn't she know it! But was it her fault? They know only one thing, though: Tedek had left the ghetto for her sake! But more than once had Tedek gone from the ghetto to the Aryan side! Ferber always used Tedek to help him on his underground missions. More than once. . . . And he had never been caught. Actually, the most ingenious ghetto plans, no matter how carefully worked out, always proved to be horribly foolish and naïve. Ghetto plans! Tedek had been obsessed with just one problem: how to get through the Beskidian Woods to the Slovakian border. As if he had nothing else to worry about. He already had an elaborate plan, thought out to the last detail, how he would take her to Palestine. But no sooner did he step out of the ghetto than he was caught. Ghetto plans! If not for her, maybe Tedek would never have even taken this disastrous step. Tedek had been in love with her. It was all clear, now. Everyone had known it but she. She had never shown any signs of such feelings toward him; it never even occurred to her. Why, she hadn't even agreed to his plan of escape because she had felt he was doing it for her, to save her. Still, how could she show her face to his family—though there's no way of knowing whether he was sent to Auschwitz, or to a labour camp. But what's the difference? Nobody knows what "Auschwitz" is, just as nobody knows what "labour camp" is. People vanish into both without a trace, and that's the last that is heard of them.

Photographs . . .

All sorts of photographs. So many photographs. Big ones and small ones drop from the ripped pockets. They lie scattered all over the floor; people walk on them. At first, when a photograph would drop out of a pocket, they'd try to read the inscription on the back. Now they don't even bother. Rivkah, the cleaning woman, sweeps them in bunches on to the rubbish heap. No one pays attention to the photographs any more: Schultze is watching; besides, the faces in the photographs no longer mean anything. One is used to their lying about underfoot: brides and grooms on their bridal day, tots smiling from their cribs, boyish heads darting their sharp, engaging glances at you.

People had taken along these photos as relics of their own lives.

The inscriptions on the backs of the photographs aren't read any more. You know without looking you won't be able to understand them, anyway. Some are inscribed in Dutch and others in French; some in Russian and others in German; some in Flemish, others in Czech; some in Greek and others in Yiddish; some in Italian, others in Hebrew. Who here knows so many languages?

". . . *A pot that feeds seven* . . ." These had been Vevke's very words that night she arrived here from Cracow, right after he had rescued her from the Jew-Militia. Tedek was still around, then. She didn't know him as yet. Menashe, too, was still around. The Five Oaks—all the sons of Vevke the cobbler—were still together then. He had told her then "*that*

10

feeds seven," and these are still his very words. For him there are still *seven* . . .

Tedek must have been out of his mind. All knew him to be cautious, realistic, and he knew very well it was the matter of the woods that had cost his younger brother Menashe his life. And what difference did it really make, the Slavic Woods or the Beskidian? Long before Menashe's death they began finding Jewish corpses that had been tossed from the Slavic Woods on to the crossroads, notes nailed to their naked flesh: SHOT, BUT NOT BY GERMANS—POLISH PARTISANS.

Tedek knew this very well, but he never stopped arguing, "I'm not waiting for the Germans to kill every Jew in the ghetto!" What hadn't she done to keep him from carrying out his plan! She pleaded with him and begged him, though never bringing up the name of his brother Menashe. She didn't dare. But Tedek's mind was made up; not even his father or his mother could change it. "It's no use," he declared. "I won't stay in the ghetto!" Vevke listened, swallowed deep, said nothing.

Then, when Tedek brought home the false report, "Menashe has joined the partisans," Vevke swallowed that same deep swallow. To this day it's hard to tell whether he really had been fooled, or whether he knew what actually had happened. His wife, Gittel, stood facing the stove, her tears dropping softly into the pots she kept shifting aimlessly from place to place. Vevke stood just behind her and spoke to her over her shoulder:

"Gittel, my crown, you'll see, Menashe will soon be back in a Russian tank as high as Heller's house. You'll see, Gittel . . ."

He got these words out, and rushed from the shack as if he were being chased.

On the high tables in the cutting room the strips of cloth brought in from the rag room are piled colour by colour: navy blue, official students' uniform; black Alpaca, worn by Orthodox Jews and accountants; blue serge, for evening wear; brown herring-bone cheviot, for a stroll on a brisk, clear winter day. Neatly assorted, colour by colour, they lie on top of each other. On each pile the cutter places his pattern, shoves the blade of his razor-sharp knife deep into the cloth, draws it along the outline of the pattern—as a pencil is drawn along a ruler's edge—and cuts "mates." The "mates"

11

are taken for sewing to the machine room and then returned to the cobblers' room.

When the Labour Commissioner first decided to open the shoe shop in the ghetto, there developed a terrific crush on the Judenrat.[1] Everyone wanted to get into the shoe shop. People scraped the last family heirlooms out of their hiding places and thrust them into the hands of the Judenrat people. For what greater security was there for a Jew than to have a labour card identifying him as a member of the Labour Force of none other than the Sonder Beauftragter—the very Labour Commissioner who was engaged in providing Jews for the labour camps! Why, it's as clear as day he won't send his own workers to a labour camp!

But it soon became evident that there were no cobblers in the ghetto—the Judenrat had early turned the poor artisans over to the Gestapo as ransom for the rich. Could they have imagined that the time would come when a cobbler would be needed in the ghetto, and for the life of them they wouldn't be able to produce one? For with "intellectuals" and "screwturners"[2] alone they could hardly make shoes for the Gestapo. So it is easy to see how relieved the Judenrat crowd were to be able to produce Vevke the Lithuanian, who was known from pre-war days as a master cobbler. And Vevke really saved the day. He was appointed technical supervisor of the shoe shop and quickly set about making shoemakers out of ghetto Jews.

Row after row of long, low tables stand in the cobblers' room. On the low benches lining the tables sit eminent doctors, famous lawyers, rabbis, all trying urgently to look to Schultze like old-time cobblers.

Sometimes it seems that here is a large kindergarten, except that on the low benches sit grown-up Jews, and instead of toys their pallid hands hold wooden soles which they rim with nails.

At noon, when Schultze disappears to the Comrades' Club for lunch, Vevke sits down at a cobblers' table and gets to work. No sooner does Vevke feel the cobblers' hammer in his hand than the old gleam is back in his eyes. He is re-

[1] Judenrat: "Jew-Council"—German-appointed autonomous Jewish Community Council.

[2] Screwturners: wealthy merchants who bought labour cards from the Judenrat and showed up at the shop only when the Germans came into the ghetto to collect Jews for deportation.

freshed, full of colour again, like one soaking in the warmth and love of home after long, lonely wandering. Vevke isn't cut out to be a boss. He's fed up with the day-long aimless circling among the tables. It saps his energy, he begins to feel listless; his feet drag, his eyes droop. All day long they shout, "Supervisor!" "Supervisor!" First from this table, then from that; now from this room, then from the other. The whole thing disgusts him. He can't stand to hear it any more, and he can no longer stand being responsible for shoes made by doctors and lawyers.

Now, gripping the hammer, he feels all his limbs come to life again. The sinews of his right arm begin to bulge, his chest expands, a surge of power fills his whole being. Ah, it's wonderful to feel this way again? Feeling nimble, he scoops a handful of nails into his mouth, like a hungry glutton, and an urge awakens within him to burst into song.

Strange. Even when you're strapped to the torture rack in the Gestapo dungeon, and the tools of death let up cracking your bones for a moment, the marrow in them suddenly gets an overpowering urge to sing out in joy—though the black uniforms still stand over you, their faces grinning satanically at you. You're still strapped to the rack—notwithstanding that, in spite of it, you have a terrific urge to grin with them. Your bones' first moment of relief impels you to it. The marrow in them suddenly wants to sing.

Gittel would surely say now, "Seventy? More like seven!" In the ghetto, in the shoe shop of the Germans, and he wants to sing! So he remains silent. He stifles the song stirring in his sinews and listens with one ear as Silverstein, the famous pediatrician, repeats the political news for Vevke the supervisor who has deigned to sit at their table. The other cobblers do not look up from their shoes; they stay huddled over their work like hens crowding around the grain just tossed at them.

"The 'box' reports that Roosevelt has spoken . . ."

"Roosevelt has spoken . . ." The cobblers pass the word along from man to man, table to table, without looking up from their shoes.

"Roosevelt has spoken . . ."

Nobody asks what he said, what tidings he brings, just as drug addicts do not ask themselves what it is that blunts their senses; what causes them to tremble so at the very mention of the white potion.

13

Enough to know "Roosevelt has spoken . . ."

Bergson, the cantor of the "atheists'" synagogue, who before the war lived in the same house as Vevke—which, in fact, explains how he came to be working in the shoe shop—charts out on the reverse side of a wooden sole the strategic situation in Perekop, in the Crimea, which the Germans are about to capture.

"A pox and a plague on them for all their power!" Vevke spits his curse out with a bunch of nails.

At the cobblers' table, Vevke forgets a while the hurt buried deep in his heart. The cobbler's hammer in his hand affects him like a magic wand. He sheds his here-and-now personality and becomes the old Vevke: no longer the "supervisor" circling among the tables, responsible to the Germans for the shoes manufactured by his "cobblers."

But this lasts only as long as Schultze is away from the shoe shop.

When he gets back, Schultze first turns to the rag room. He slinks stealthily in, so no one will see him. His skull is a bloated white globe, without a trace of hair from nape to eyes. A wrinkled hint of a face peers from his bloated skull as if it had been attached as an afterthought. Altogether, his head looks like a magnified embryo head. His mouth is never idle. There is always a lighted cigar pegged between his blue, tight lips. Smoke rises ceaselessly from the cigar, as if some special instinct were constantly pressing him, prodding him: "Show them you are Schultze! Show them you're not an embryo! Fact is, you smoke cigars."

Schultze has a game leg; which is why he moves about on three. And it is the third leg—his cane—that is the most dangerous. The tip of the cane has a rubber cap, which only Schultze knows how to wield so it will be a long time before his victim regains his breath. No one knows yet whether the secret of the cane's evil power is in the rubber tip or in Schultze's ability to aim his third leg. However that may be, Schultze slinks into the rag room, convinced that no one sees him. And actually, it is possible that no one would notice him, if the smell of his burning cigar didn't carry such a long way.

He sneaks first into the rag room. He has already sent two seam rippers to Auschwitz. One had found a Russian gold "porker" under the knee patch of a pair of overalls. Her neighbour insisted she was entitled to half: she had held the

14

overalls first. She certainly will not give up her share of the coin! The argument reached Schultze's ears, and right after work they were both turned over to the Gestapo—never to return. The next day, Schultze issued an order that all seam rippers were to be thoroughly searched before leaving work. But they outsmarted him, and if anyone did find anything in those days, she quickly swallowed it. From that day on, the seam rippers have been keeping a close watch on each other's mouths.

II

The photograph lay on the floor at her feet. It had fallen from the breast pocket of a jacket together with a small phylactery bag. The bag was a purple velvet, embroidered with a silver monogram inside a Star of David. Daniella glided the cobbler's knife along the seam of a checked winter coat, like a violinist tuning a string—not really playing, but a deaf man only sees the motions; she isn't really working, but Schultze watching from afar won't know the difference. She couldn't tear her eyes from the photo. A boy and a girl. Just like she and Moni in the photo set in the locket on her heart. The eyes of the two children looked up at her from the floor, giving her no rest. As if they were Moni's eyes asking, *"Dani, why did you go away?"*

Her past wreathed itself about the photograph on the floor like a frame and looked up at her as out of some strange, hazy existence. Her own life now lay at the foot of the heap of old jackets and trousers: her own life, her own yesterday. Yet she couldn't make it out. It was so alien to this rag room; so remote from the high cutting tables and from the low tables in the cobblers' room! The people in the rooms suddenly seemed like creatures enclosed in a coloured crystal ball: to all appearances alive, astir, but she can't reach through to them. She is very far from them, beyond their sphere, unable to approach them, mingle with them—yet here she is among them. Her life lies at the foot of the heap of old clothes, wisps of recollection floating to the top of her consciousness like Schultze's cigar smoke rising into the room. You can't see the smoke, but you sense its terrifying Germanic smell.

Two existences. Severed and sundered. No connection or

bridge between them. Which is reality and which nightmare? This clothes heap certainly is no mirage: she sees it with her eyes, feels it with her hands! Can she be living these two separate lives simultaneously? Two existences, one along-side the other?—"*War is brewing . . . It's a bad time for excursions . . .*" Daddy waving a white kerchief . . . the train pulling out . . .—How does Schultze's head suddenly loom here in the doorway? How did she herself get here? Where is the bridge between these two existences? What are the blue checks on this winter coat in her hands? What is the mean-ing of this knife gleam she's now pressing into a seam? . . .

The purple of the phylactery bag splashes against her eyes. Everything fills with purple. A terrific urge fills her to pick up this little bag. But Rivkah sweeps such trifles on to the rubbish heap: you can't cut any "mates" from such a small bag. Her diary is also bound in the same purple velvet. On the bronze plaque is inscribed: *To My Gifted Daniella. . . .* A diagonal scar now creases these words, as if the German bullet had intended to erase them. The bullet would have ploughed into her back if she hadn't taken the diary along in her knapsack, and she would have been left lying in Yablova market-place as all the other Jews were left lying there; as all her first-term classmates were left lying there.

In the cutting room the section heads bustle from table to table. The pressure is on. The "screwturners" turned out full force in the factory today: an Aktion must be brewing. The assorted strips of smooth cloth lie in neat piles on the floor—like Yablova market-place when the Germans ordered the Jews to fall flat on their faces. All at once, the market-place was paved with human backs, like neat piles of cloth: now the market-place was full, suddenly it was empty—at once full and empty. Not the way it was on the road to Cracow; then, she wasn't able to catch even a glimpse of the road. Only when the German bombers swooped down, and all swarmed to the shelter of the ditches along the road, only then did a stark, endless road emerge, stripped of its human casing. Then she saw: a horse carcass, legs outstretched— the people had trampled it to death; a broken bicycle lying on its side, wheels facing skyward; baby carriages groaning under pots and bedding—a bare, dead, endless road.

. . . Can these be the clothes of the Yablova Jews? Reesha Meyerchik wore a coat just like this on the excursion. If not for the bronze plaque on her diary they might be ripping her

16

own raincoat in this rag room. But how did the clothes of the Yablova Jews get here? It all happened three years ago! Mommy had urged her, "Dani, take along your raincoat. It will come in handy during the trip. . . ." If she hadn't taken it along she wouldn't be able to smuggle Abram the trader's cloth wrapped around her waist, and she would have starved to death. There's no question that an Aktion is scheduled in the ghetto: why else did Berman the gold dealer come scampering to the workshop? The cutters work their hearts out. They are on their feet at their table all day. Vevke, too, plods about on his feet all day. If not for Vevke, she could never have dreamed of working in the shoe shop. She's a lucky one, always was. How else explain that she's still alive?

A day of letters, written and unwritten. A letter drops from almost every pocket today. As if the people had all been members of the same transport;[1] or as if they had been assured that they would be permitted to write home as soon as they were brought to their destination. Rivkah sweeps the letters on to the rubbish heap. The envelopes still pulse with the life of the fingers that had sealed them.

A strange fear now hovers over the rag room. Everyone feels it. Suddenly, the jacket linings begin to exude human body heat; hands fill out the sleeves; necks sprout from all collars; stomachs and legs materialize in all the trousers. Live humans fill the clothes.

A numb silence suddenly settles among the seam rippers, the knife blades move as of their own accord. Eyes are lowered to the seam, and the strange garment reflects back at them their own doom.

On one of the windows in the rag room, over a broken pane, a prayer shawl is spread, fixed with nails to the window frame, to keep out the snow. The wind humps itself into the shawl, and it looks like a Jew wrapped in a prayer shawl straining to jump through the window.

As the women sit in stunned silence, the thunder rumbles down from the machine room with mounting intensity. As if lava has begun seething within the clothes heap and is about to burst out and swamp everything, everyone. Schultze stands near the doorway and with the rubber tip of his cane shoves a letter on to the rubbish heap.

"Zara!" he screeches at Rivkah (to Schultze all Jewish women are "Sara"). "Let's have it clean!" He raises his

---

[1] Transport: deportation to death camp.

17

cane, sets the rubber tip against the centre of Rivkah's brow, pauses momentarily, peers into the woman's eyes, and suddenly, as if remembering something, resumes his violent screeching: "Clean! Clean!"

And he goes hobbling out of the rag room.

A day of letters. Some written in ink; others, in pencil. Either way, no one can read them. Maybe they are written in Dutch, maybe in Greek. The truth is, you're afraid to read them, let alone pocket them. It may be forbidden. Who knows what Schultze forbids and what he allows! He has sent people to Auschwitz for pettier crimes. *"Now don't forget, Daniella, to send home a postcard every day. . . ."* Papa had never looked so worried as that time in the railway station. She hadn't understood, then; she had other things on her mind. Later, in the Cracow ghetto, they frightened her with their admonishment: "God forbid that a Jew should use the German mail!" Everything connected with the swastika reeked of death. "The war won't last for ever. Better wait; better be careful . . ." She could still have written home, then. Kongressia ghetto hadn't been so hermetically sealed. Later she got the report from Zalke the smuggler. God! How casually Zalke stated: Nothing new in Kongressia ghetto. The living—aren't dead; the dead— aren't alive. No, he doesn't know her parents. Find someone in the ghetto? Not a chance! No one lives where they used to. Even the dead don't have an address any more. No one even has a name any more. "Jew" is what pegs them all. Comes an Aktion and the German reaches into the ghetto as into a seed bag and pulls out a fistful; every seed that slips between the fingers gets a bit of a reprieve inside the gloomy sack . . .

Why did she let them sway her? Why didn't she write to her parents then, when they were still at home? Two years in Cracow. Strange, not once during those two years did it occur to her that in that very city, almost within a stone's throw, was the King's Palace, the Vavel. The whole purpose of the excursion had been the Vavel. How could she forget! *"Vavel . . ."* Overnight the name had taken on a meaning of dread. It clung to you day and night, making wakefulness a terror and sleep a nightmare.

It was from the Vavel that Gauleiter Frank extended the rule of the German people.

Vavel. How hearts used to quicken at the sound of the

18

name. Vavel—Mickiewicz's tomb. How could she forget! As if it happened in another existence. So remote, so alien to everything about her now. A beautiful dream—gone, forgotten. But it still ripples through her being, softly, tenderly, like the lingering, dying whisper of a harp-string; like the haunting echo of a melody of yearning . . .

A melody of another world. . . .

2

A BRIGHT world, radiant as an early-spring morning. A world full of mystic lures that beckon to young hearts. Summer's end, 1939.

DANIELLA PRELESHNIK.

She, the fourteen-year-old schoolgirl, could not fall asleep that night before her first excursion. She was seized with her first travel fever. The thoughts raced in and out of her mind as through a swinging door, leaving her keyed up with anticipation: tomorrow, first thing in the morning, she is leaving for Cracow with her classmates on her very first excursion. How she had to fight to get her way! Finally she prevailed upon papa, who kept arguing: "It's a bad time for excursions. . . . War is brewing. . . ." What has a war to do with a school excursion to Mickiewicz's tomb in the Vavel? Today is August 27, and on September 3, when the new school year begins, the class will already be back. So what's there to be afraid of? Those who want war don't have to go on the excursion. But she—how does all that concern her?

Beyond the window, the streets of Poland's industrial city Kongressia began drowsing off to sleep. A night tram whizzed by from time to time, grinding its wheels against the tracks— you don't hear their clangour at all when they race through the city's bustling streets during the day.

A full moon tarried on the crucifix spire of the church which the Jewish industrialist, Oskar Kahanov, built for his workers beside his large factory. A pale beam of light streamed through the open window into the elegant, white-lacquered children's room, illuminating the packed knapsack on the table. On the other side of the moonbeam rose the soft, rhythmic breathing of sleeping Moni, Daniella's seven-year-old brother.

19

. . . What a wonderful chance this will be to stop off in Metropoli and visit Harry. She'll go through with her plan even if it means missing the first day of school. Maybe she'll convince Harry to take her with him to Palestine now. He promised to send for her as soon as he got there; so why shouldn't he take her along in the first place? Of course, Mum and Dad mustn't get wind of all this.

Daniella loves her brother Harry heart and soul. She idolizes him. Though he seems to have become somewhat estranged lately. Since Sanya came into his life, he has been slow to answer her letters. And his letters don't even sound the same. No question about it. He is completely absorbed with this stranger. Sanya stands like a wall between Harry and her. True, he doesn't say as much; but you only have to compare his early letters, so long and meaningful you actually had to study them, with the postcards he's been sending her lately. Each postcard opens and closes with the same excuse: he's busy preparing for his coming trip to Palestine. Harry's visits, too, have become less and less frequent since he met Sanya. In the old days, when he used to visit, he would take her on long walks, ask her to concerts. Wintertime, they'd go ice-skating together. Often, he would spring surprises on her. Leaving school after class, she would suddenly spot Harry waiting for her across the street. He would come up to her, gracefully doff his hat, and say, "May I have the honour of the mademoiselle's company for a brief afternoon promenade?"

The girls wouldn't stop talking about him for days after that.

Daniella tossed and turned in her bed. Strange fantasies, often taking on a hue of reality, wove and spun before her eyes, weaving her into them. On another sleepless midnight like this, she would surely turn on her desk lamp and sit down to write in her diary: at any other time, she wouldn't be afraid that Mum might see the light in the window of the children's-room door. More than once has Ma come into the room at midnight to take away a book she was reading, or close the diary she was writing in, and send her off to bed. Tonight she can't take a chance: tomorrow is the excursion, and Pa still isn't too keen on her going. Any mischief now, and she'll really spoil everything.

She must have the diary on the excursion. This time she's got to win first prize in the essay contest at school. She'll put

20

her best into her description of the excursion. But she won't show anyone her essay. Except Harry—she'll send him a copy. She must surprise him. She must win first prize. Then Harry will know whom to be proud of.

She jumped out of bed, opened the desk drawer and took out the diary: tomorrow she might forget to put it in her knapsack. The moonbeam illuminated the thick notebook in her hands. It was bound in ornate purple velvet, and on the binding gleamed a small bronze plaque, shaped like a calling card, inscribed: *To My Gifted Daniella, From Your Brother Harry.*

She began leafing through the book:

Schoolboys and schoolgirls, now on their summer vacation, take frequent walks in the city park. Some lean over the wooden bridge on the lake and toss bits of bread to the snow-white swan gliding across the mirror of water like a serene princess ensconced in reverie. From the expression on her face you can tell she regards herself queen of this realm: the park and all of us standing around belong to her. The sky and sun are her companions; the stars, her playmates. She passes the time of day with them, and has them over for an occasional soirée, when the moon drops in for a dip. She doesn't need the benevolence of mere humans. But when boys and girls throw crumbs into her lake, she comes drifting lackadaisically over to the bridge, imperiously scans the scene about her, plunges her noble bill deep, deep into the water and draws it up with a white bowlike flourish. She doesn't chew—lest she be suspected of beggary—but gracefully swallows her prey and goes sailing majestically back across her mirror-lake—a proud pauper.

Opaline veils of sleep fluttered over Daniella's long eyelashes. Out of the darkness of the park the white swan floats toward her. The long moonbeam streaming through the window flares into a lake. The swan twins itself. A brace of swans float near a long wooden bridge. Daniella stands on an unknown shore. The lake is a maelstrom of red and black. Behind her back, countless trains prance and reel. The train engines have faces, like leering drunkards. They grind screeching slaughter knives into rails. Daniella wants to flee. She wants to save herself. But she can't. As if she were running

21

against a gale. Her feet lift heavily, as though running under water. She turns around: Harry stands amid hordes of bristling slaughter knives. Everything is red, crimson red. Around him, at him, myriad heads of drunken train guards guffaw through gaping maws. Knots of sparkling smoke belch and billow from the train chimneys towards the crimson-dark skies. Harry grows taller—taller—he towers above the smokestacks, his head reaching the sky. A white cloud enshrouds him. Pinions him. His petrified eyes gape at her. Trains with tall smokestacks start chasing her, breathing their terrifying clangour at her. The clangs burst through the open window into the children's room, reaching out to seize her and drag her outside. The brace of swans suddenly spread white wings, beckon her to come to them: they will give her shelter. Daniella runs. The way is long. The nearer she gets the further they recede. She stumbles. She is about to fall. She struggles frantically to reach them. She screams. But the scream sticks in her throat. Suddenly she feels herself plunging off a great height into a bottomless void, falling . . . falling . . .

As Daniella opened her eyes, the clangour of the train still rang through the night. Her heart pounded violently. A cold sweat covered her brow. Her feet felt weary, as if she had really just been running with them. The fear still clutched at her, the dream lingered before her eyes—a real, living thing. The fear, too, was real.

The moon shaft no longer lay on the table. It now gleamed sharp and angular through a corner of the open window directly at her head, appearing like a long, steel-sharp javelin piercing her temples, and pinned in the wall beside her bed.

II

The sky was a sheen of azure over Kongressia's high chimneys. A late August sun lavished its rays on the grey asphalt streets on which the first-term girls of Knowledge High School marched to the train. A soft breeze spun merry ribbons of sun through the bobbing ranks of girlish heads.

Daniella paraded in the first rank, brimming with joy: her first excursion. What an adventure, what a cultural experience it's going to be! With her own eyes she will see her beloved Mickiewicz, almost all of whose poems she can recite by heart. But best of all will be her surprise meeting with Harry!

She isn't too sure yet how she will carry out this rendezvous. Originally, she thought she'd wire him to meet her at the Metropoli station. But no, if Harry knows she's coming it will spoil the surprise. Best to arrive in Metropoli unexpected, wait near Harry's home, and when she sees him coming out, follow him a few steps, draw up alongside him and with feigned indifference let fall, "Is m'lord inclined to take a forlorn maiden for a brief afternoon promenade?"

Oh, how delicious it will be!

She marches airily along, her feet lifting eagerly as if in step with a lilting rhythm. Her knapsack is fastened to her back; she doesn't feel it. Her raincoat is folded over her knapsack. Ma had insisted she take it along, and this time she didn't dare disobey.

Fourteen-year-old Daniella trips along. Sport boots laced high over her shapely legs, tawny face glowing in the sun, long, dark lashes shading her dreamy sky-blue eyes.

Heads of relatives appear at the passing windows and balconies. Youngsters shout, "The first term is going on an excursion!" School children look enviously on. Mothers wave white kerchiefs. Tots gesture with their little hands, calling out girls' names. The marching heads send up blithe, elated farewell glances, and from the windows and balconies come the parting replies, "Pleasant trip!" "Have a good time! . . ."

Preleshnik, though he had parted with his daughter before leaving for his office that morning, was uneasy. A strange feeling prodded him to return home and again admonish Daniella not to forget to send home a postcard every day, letting them know how and where she was. Back in the house, he found Daniella already gone. An untidy emptiness showed from the children's room. Only her locket gleamed on the edge of the desk. In her haste she had apparently forgotten to slip it around her neck.

Daniella had received the locket as a thirteenth-birthday gift from her father. Within the locket, in twin gold oval frames, were set two miniature portraits; one of her parents; the other of Daniella with her brother Moni—Daniella in her school uniform, two blonde white-ribboned braids tumbling down to her breast. Beside her, on a round straw-table, sat three-year-old Moni, in a white sailor suit, his velvet eyes rounded at the queer black picture box in front of him.

Preleshnik took the locket from the desk to bring it to Daniella at the station and, by the way, tell her again what was on his mind. But suddenly he heard Moni weeping in the next room: Daniella had only just left, and he already missed his sister.

Moni was seven years old, and of just the opposite nature from Daniella. He didn't like leaving the house; the world outside held no attraction for him. He even had to be bribed into going for a walk. Moni had his mother's soft, velvety eyes. These were the eyes with which his father had fallen in love at first sight. Generations of rabbinical aristocracy shone in them. Often, when Preleshnik saw his son's eyes puckered up at him, he scooped him into his big arms, hugged him tight, frolicked with him on the sofa, and nuzzled the little body, exclaiming rapturously, "My little monkey face! My pure little cherub!"

Seeing his father in the doorway, Moni burst into a fit of tears and rushed into his father's outstretched arms. Preleshnik lifted him, snuggled the tear-soaked face to his cheek, his lips, his eyes, and murmured soothingly, "What is it, my little cherub? What's this crying about?"

". . . want Dani," the child sobbed.

So Preleshnik decided to take Moni along to the station to say goodbye to his sister again.

On the main platform, they found the girls waiting to go, their knapsacks at their feet. The train has been delayed: the rails were commandeered by troop transports. When Daniella saw her father and little brother in the distance, she ran toward them, hugged Moni and kissed him.

"Dani, why are you going away?" Moni asked sadly.

"To bring you a nice present, my pet."

On the rails before them, long trains reached off into the horizon: countless cars, some open on all sides, others closed. On one of the open cars, soldiers in white undershirts puttered about large steaming cauldrons, preparing lunch. Near the soup cauldrons, an accordion wheezed in the hands of a soldier sitting propped against a queer machine gun whose long barrel aimed skyward.

Preleshnik didn't like this news of the train's delay at all. But he tried to keep an impassive face, so as not to dampen his daughter's spirits. He merely reminded her—since she had a tendency to forget, when, as her mother put it, the "confusing Muse" possessed her—to send home a postcard every

24

day; and not to forget that as she had forgotten her locket on the desk.

When the train finally pulled in, a gust of exhilaration swept through the girls. They clattered into the coaches. Daniella's head immediately appeared in one of the open coach windows. The sky danced in the blueness of her eyes, and a sunny comb of breeze swept gaily through her golden tresses.

The train started. Preleshnik and Moni, with them the station and all within it, slowly receded. Daniella's eyes were riveted on her father: one hand waved a white kerchief high above his head, the other held on to Moni.

The train moved gradually off. A grey emptiness unfurled rapidly between the endless ribs of railway lines.

Daniella stood watching a long while, and her eyes cached the scene away for ever.

3

THE first to go on the German pyre were the Jewish town-lets in Poland.

The District of Metropoli was subdivided by the Germans into several isolated "Jew-Quarters," each with its own German-appointed Judenrat. Movement from one quarter to the other was prohibited. If a fugitive Jew from one of the nearby empty ravaged ghettos was caught in Metropoli, the Gestapo immediately deported him to Auschwitz. But if the Judenrat's Jew-Militia caught such a Jew, they either turned him immediately over to the Gestapo, or for a ransom allowed him to stay at one of the specially set up Assembly Centres, where they concentrated those whose identity cards lacked the Gestapo's red swastika stamp authorizing them to stay in the District of Metropoli.

The militia concentrated the illegals in this manner so that if the Germans caught an illegal and demanded an explanation, the Judenrat could excuse itself: "We know all about these scum. We're only rounding them up so as to turn them over in batches to the Gestapo."

These illegals, therefore, were forbidden to sleep, let alone live, with their relatives or in any other private home. Any-one caught in such a crime was immediately shipped, together with his hosts, to Auschwitz.

25

Metropoli, 16-2-42

My dreams and my plans. My heart had spun them with the first gossamer threads of fantasy. Plans about my trip to Palestine . . . plans about the moment my feet would touch Metropoli for the first time. Simply to walk into Harry's house—this, I thought, was not enough. Better to wait for him outside and surprise him. I already knew the thrill of such a happy moment; I experienced it myself when Harry used to wait for me near school. He's the one who taught it to me.

"*. . . Ardent wishes teeming in the human heart are like seeds ejected into the invisible womb of the cosmos. They flower for the most part, but usually in such a form that the conceiving heart no longer recognizes them . . .*"

These words come back to my mind every time I recall my first night in Metropoli, after Zalke the smuggler left me standing among the dark ghetto alleys. He agreed to take me out of Cracow ghetto on one condition: since he had to smuggle two loaves of bread to a poor relative in Metropoli, I would have to help him by carrying a loaf. It seemed such a small thing. What is a loaf of bread, or a thousand loaves for that matter, against the prospect of finally being together with Harry!

"Mr. Zalke!" I said, "It won't be any trouble for me to take even both loaves, I assure you."

"No!" he snapped. "Two loaves the Germans will nab at the border!" The main thing is, he kept drumming at me, if I'm caught, I mustn't forget I'm an Aryan heading for Metropoli to look for a job. The bread? I found it. Didn't buy it; didn't get it. Found it. Found it near the railway lines; that's why it's so grimy. Also: never in my life saw Zalke; never ever heard of him.

Later it turned out that the bread I was taking to Zalke's poor relative was full of diamonds and American dollar bills.

"*. . . Ardent wishes teeming in the human heart flower, for the most part . . .*" But when I first stepped into Metropoli, I completely forgot the golden fantasies my heart once spun about the moment of my arrival here. Just as it never dawned on me in Cracow that it was the site of the Vavel. Yes, my ardent wish came true—only instead

26

of coming to poet Mickiewicz's Vavel, I came to the Vavel of Gauleiter Frank. The same happened the night I arrived in Metropoli. It completely slipped my mind that this was Harry's home, and I remembered only that I must keep close to the dark walls of the ghetto shacks so a German patrol shouldn't spot me.

Will this be culmination of my dreams?

That night, Monyek Matroz, head of the Judenrat, ordered the Jew-Militia to take Vevke the cobbler from his bed and bring him to militia headquarters: the Gestapo big-shots demand flashy, new, cork-soled shoes as gifts for their ladies. "Cork shoes like the high-falutin' Yid bitches used to wear!" And who but the master cobbler Vevke would be able to fill the order to the satisfaction of the Gestapo mes-dames?

In the militia orderly room of Jew-Quarter 3, the orderly of the day sprawled deep in an ornate leather armchair, one foot dangling over the upholstered arm of the chair. His blue-white cap cocked to one side and his eyes half asleep, he continued drawling indifferently toward Vevke, "People'd give a mint to be able to cross such a border. God protects fools? Well, what happened? This fool kid heads straight for militia headquarters. Beats me how such a gosling ever got out of Cracow ghetto, got in here, and they never spotted her."

"What will you do with her?" Vevke asked.

The militiaman didn't budge from his snug berth. He didn't even look at Daniella, as though it were not she they were discussing.

"Whaddya mean, 'what'?" he grunted through his heavy eyelids. "Tomorrow she shoves off with the transport."

In the split second that a ghetto dweller forfeits his life, in that split second does he sometimes retrieve it. And both are chance occurrences. By promising to sew new leather soles on the militiaman's boots, Vevke saved Daniella's life. He immediately took her to the Centre at Heller's house, where he and his family lived in a hovel in the third court.

II

Daniella went down to the gate of the house.

Sunday mornings, right after the militia has checked to

see that none of the "illegals" are missing, Daniella can't stay put in her bed. Though the night curfew is still taut over the ghetto streets, and it is prohibited to step out, Daniella can't resist going to the gate. For Sundays, Harry comes to her from Jew-Quarter 1. Sundays they don't work in the factories. Sundays the Germans carouse in the taverns and it is easier for Harry to slink through the fields and come to her in Jew-Quarter 3. It's less dangerous, Sundays.

The corridor leaving the house was already filled with human shadows. A dank air chilled the bones. Daniella turned up the collar of her raincoat. She thought she would surely be the first to get here. She thinks so every Sunday dawn. But as soon as she enters the dark corridor, she senses that its walls are already draped with human shadows, mutely waiting to dash out under the lifting curfew. Someone approaches the gate, opens it, and immediately rustles back into place. You don't see him any more, just as you don't see a shadow melting into a dark corner.

The dead, dark street peered through the open gate. The curfew stretched across the ghetto like a black blanket. A foul endless mizzle of snow-clotted rain smudged the darkness. What was her rush to get here? If not for the snow, she could hurry to the Judenrat soup-kitchen as soon as the curfew lifts, and in the compound there, near the fields, watch for Harry's arrival. Though it's senseless: Harry is hardly ever here before noon. She herself constantly urges and cautions him not to dare leave his Jew-Quarter earlier. By noon, the Germans are already plastered and the trip is not so dangerous. Strange: though she constantly begs Harry not to come too soon, she always rushes off to the compound as soon as the curfew lifts and stands there waiting, looking, her eyes straining to make out the little dot moving toward her from the foot of the low mountain, moving closer, larger, clearer. Strange: even from afar she always knows when it's Harry coming; his dot is different from the others. If only he won't come too soon. If she could see Sanya, she would tell her not to let him leave before noon. Her heart tells her it will all wind up in disaster. If she could only make Harry stop coming altogether! Oh, God—

The gate stood open. The night curfew lay over the stooped ghetto shacks like a lid over a gloomy pot. A moist snow hovered in mid-air as if it had drowsed off to sleep on the

28

way down. Daniella snuggled closer to the corridor wall, out of the way of the draught.

. . . As soon as she earns a few marks, she'll go right to a cobbler and get herself some new half-soles. Oh no, not to Vevke! Even if she knows her feet will rot she won't go to Vevke! Vevke won't let her pay. Seems Hayim-Idl brought in some merchandise yesterday, a bundle of felts. Maybe she'll be able to make some money there. No chance of making any money after work at the shop. Before you turn around it's curfew time. If she doesn't fix her shoes in time, she'll be left barefooted. Sunday is the only day you can earn anything from Hayim-Idl. But by the time she gets back from the soup kitchen, the day will be over. Maybe she should go back to the Centre now and ask Hayim-Idl if he has anything for her. She could still pick up a few marks before noon, before she runs off to meet Harry. Hayim-Idl is probably still asleep. What a bungler she is! Others manage to get everything done, while she—all the time in the world doesn't seem to be enough for her. If she were more alert, she could still make some money before noon. But what if Harry shows up earlier? Oh, Hayim-Idl would surely have told her last night if he had anything for her. She's not sorry he refused to take Sanya's shoes. They're selling everything they have for bread. All Harry has left is the suit he wears. They'll be able to feed themselves for a week with Sanya's shoes. Brand new shoes. Mommy told her to wear the high sport boots on the excursion. Good thing she obeyed. She obeyed everything, then, only they should let her go. Now, she's at least able to keep her feet warm inside the high tops. She must remember to put new laces on her shoes today. They always manage to get knotted up in the morning, when she's in a hurry to get to the shop. What a bungler she is!

A little bead of flame glows somewhere in a corner. Someone draws long and deep on a cigarette. The ember flares and immediately wanes. The cigarette in the dark is still and so is the man behind it.

The corridor is like a shadow-filled subterranean tunnel. The shadows are mute. Each has been startled from his bed by his own calamity. All wait for the curfew to lift so they will be able to rush out: one to the Judenrat, another to a "fixer" who arranges things for a price. Each wants to find out if the husband, the wife, the son—taken from them yesterday—is still in the ghetto; if, so long as they haven't been deported as yet from the ghetto, they'll still be able to catch a glimpse of them.

Across the street, mute heads poke out of the house gates, watch apprehensively for the sight of someone on the street, for a sign that it is permissible for them to leave. Now there is not a sign of life anywhere, as if the ghetto had breathed its last. Silence. But with the first glimmer of dawn, the shadows will spring to life and tear out of all the gates. One will start running and all the others will tear out after him. Grief, but a moment ago pent within the houses, will stampede out of the gates and fill the streets of the Jew-Quarter with its dread.

Now, the shadows wait for the day to break. But day is in no hurry to shine on the ghetto. As if it weren't worth its while.

In the evening, at 5 o'clock, the gates are shut again. As curfew time approaches, running feet again stampede through the streets. The Germans stalk their prey from every nook and cranny. Anyone as much as a split-second late never gets home again. Greenberg the watchmaker from across the street was caught by a German just a few steps from his home. The next morning his wife probably stood there, feverishly waiting to run out: perhaps she'll be able to get a last look at him.

In the evening, at five o'clock, grief is again locked up in the houses. Glum and morbid, it crawls down the cramped walls, bends over the person and reaches the cup of sorrow to his lips.

The corridor fills with more and more shadows. She might as well go up to the Centre. When they all rush off, she'll be left behind, alone, anyway. Where and how will she go? A few steps and her shoes will be soaked with slush. And what'll she do at the soup kitchen compound now? In Jew-Quarter I Harry isn't even allowed to step out of his house gate yet. So what was the hurry to get down here? Up in the Centre they're all probably still asleep. If only she could sleep. If she could at least turn on the light upstairs. It's the darkness that drives her out of there. Here, in the corridor, the darkness is different. Here the darkness breathes.

Silent shadows follow each other out of the courts and as silently vanish into the darkness of the corridor. Three courts. Amazing how many people have been fitted into Heller's house. Each of the three courts must hold as many

Jews as lived on her street in Kongressia. And there must be as many Jews living in the three courts as in the whole Jewish townlet before the war. Why, she saw all the Yablova Jews herded into the market-place. *"All Jews out! Everyone to the market-place!"* The class mistress was all ready to take the girls out with them to the Germans: "We haven't done the Germans any wrong! After all, they're human beings! Surely they'll understand!" But the young Jew who had come running in from the roads that morning begged her, "For God's sake, don't open that gate!" The Germans soon battered down the gate, anyway. In the teachers' room in Kongressia, Viernik had fulminated, "It's all a lot of stock-exchange horror propaganda! There will be no war!" As if it were all up to him. As if the whole world were no more than a classroom, all the people schoolgirls, and he their schoolmaster. "At the last teachers' meeting we decided on an excursion, and an excursion there will be!" he wound up primly.

Germans.

It was the first time she had ever seen Germans. None of the girls had ever in her life seen a German. "Why should the Germans want to harm them?" the class mistress couldn't understand. Viernik's head thudded to the floor of the stair vestibule. A second ago he was standing with all the others. How did the Germans ever spy him from outside? He had barely peeped through a corner of the stair window. The pane wasn't even shattered; only a tiny round puncture by its edge, and on the wall opposite— crumpled plaster splashed with brain.

A small boy comes out of the courtyard, a large empty sack slung over his shoulder. His legs are sunk, knees and all, in a pair of crude, oversize boots. He sloshes the boots noisily along the wet cobblestones, approaches the corridor and halts briefly by the entrance. Only then does Daniella recognize him: Shlamek! The son of the man on whose brow the Germans had branded the word JUDE. He came to this court several months ago, tagging after his mother as she supported his mangled father. He looked to be about six or seven, then. Now he looks like a stunted Ghetto-Jew. Sometimes she thinks she's also grown old and grey. But when she looks in the mirror, she sees she is prettier than ever and her blonde hair richer and curlier.

The boy with the sack on his shoulder goes into the

dark corridor, parks himself somewhere, and is no longer visible. The darkness of the spot where he vanished spreads before Daniella's eyes, and like white contours of dense blackness the loose tops of Shlamek's boots are outlined above his knees. His father's exposed face when the towel slipped off his bleeding head. That day, Shlamek's father had returned home to ask the Germans for permission to take out a bed and blanket for his boy. The Germans set upon him with white-hot irons and branded JUDE across his brow and HEIL HITLER! across his chest. Only then did they let him out of his apartment. When the Judenrat was rounding up all the ghetto sick for a transport, Shlamek's father, before mounting the van, slipped off his boots and thrust them into the boy's hands: "Shlamek, take care of Mama. Don't . . ."

Near by, someone moves out of the darkness, walks over to the gate, cranes his neck into the street, comes back to his former place, as though recognizing it in the dark. A damp draught comes sweeping from the court into the dark corridor, runs icy fingers over the bodies of the standing shadows. The skin shivers at the touch. The wind lets go a rakish whistle and breezes out the gate into the empty street, as if to flaunt its freedom from curfew regulations.

Outside, the moist snow hovers in mid-air as though it has drowsed off to sleep on the way down. Daniella wonders why she is standing there: in any case she won't be running out with all the others.

She draws up her coat collar and returns to the Centre.

III

The candle was flickering under the tin cup. Dvortche stood in the corner, her back to the room, warming some breakfast in the cup for the baby. Her shadow waggling on the nearby wall looked like Lindner, the giant black-uniformed Gestapoman, storming in through the Centre wall, reaching long arms at her throat.

Hayim-Idl in his white underwear was bent over the open chest. The curtain of his "villa" was drawn to the side. He was puttering in his "store," laying the felts out on the floor, studying their colours by the fluttering candlelight, and laying them neatly upon each other. He unwound the hatbands from their wooden spools, noted down their lengths, put

32

them back in the chest and out again on the floor, as if he revelled in the mere sorting of the merchandise. Daniella sat on the edge of her bed, wearing her raincoat collar up-turned. She couldn't decide whether Hayim-Idl would have any work for her today.

Hayim-Idl is a pious young man, a go-getter. He managed to escape from his town with his wife and baby at the height of an Aktion. It's inconceivable how he managed to slip out at the last minute, carrying the eleven-month-old infant on his arm. It was during this flight that Dvortche, his wife, was suddenly struck deaf.

Hayim-Idl deals in whatever comes his way—just so there is always a piece of bread in his "villa." Today he happens to be a felt dealer: unfinished men's and women's hats, leather and satin hatbands. As soon as Hayim-Idl came to live at the Centre he set up a Spanish wall in a corner of the room, and he lives there with his family, he says, as in a private villa of their own. He has a kitchen there, he says, a dining-room, a bedroom, a children's room for little Bella, and, above all, the store. The chest serves at one and the same time as table, dining-room, and store.

When Hayim-Idl has to pick up merchandise from a dealer or deliver to customers, Daniella wraps the sheets of felt around her midriff, girds them with several rows of hatbands, and carries the hot goods under cover of her wide raincoat through the ghetto streets. For this Hayim-Idl pays her hand-somely. Both know well what is involved if she is caught—not merely loss of money, but loss of life.

On the bed opposite Daniella sits Hanna of Chebin, her closed prayer book in her lap. She looks to the dark window panes for dawn to break, when she will be allowed to start her morning prayers. Her delicate face is closed and there is wistful sadness in her eyes. Tzivia, Hanna's younger sister, sits at the other end of the bed, one elbow propped on the bedboard, her chin cupped in the palm of the other hand, musing at little Bella playing on the floor with the dilapidated man's shoe the Oswiencim girl had brought along when she came here.

The two sisters had fled here one midnight from an Aktion in Chebin. Both girls are devout former members of "Daughters of Jacob" who unfailingly say their prayers three times a day. Gentle, undefiled souls. The two sisters have a brother in Jew-Quarter 1, Abram the trader; also a God-

33

fearer on the face of it. But were a customer to turn up for God's own Throne of Glory, Abram would immediately sell him the Throne together with its Occupant. Actually, the girls had fled to Metropoli only because their brother lives here. But not only does Abram not help them, he exploits them. Instead of a mattress, they sleep on sheets of Abram's pre-war quality goods; and instead of a quilt, they cover themselves with twelve yards of doubled-over material, sewn together at the edges and sheathed in a coloured blanket cover. Abram feels secure about his merchandise here at the Centre: the Germans would never dream of searching here. More than once have they ransacked his home, since it was rumoured at the stock exchange that high-quality pre-war stuff was available at Abram's. But God in His Mercy sent Abram's sisters to pull him out of a tight spot. What would he have done if not for Hanna and Tzivia at the Centre? With money and pull, Abram fixed himself a transit pass, and he now travels from one Jew-Quarter to the next peddling his goods. Sometimes he remembers to dole his silent sisters a few marks. He is always in a hurry, intentionally or unintentionally. He wheezes into the Centre and snatches a piece of goods from the girls' bed—or throws one into it. Always the same refrain: "Customer's waiting—" "Dealer's waiting—" He never has a moment for an extra word with his sisters. It might run into money.

Abram has a son, eight-year-old Benyek. The little one is already a full-fledged assistant in his father's business. Benyek is a handsome boy, alert and sharp. He can get six yards of cloth around his belly and damned if a German eye will notice it. When Benyek sometimes comes with his father to the Centre, he remarks, "Papa, Aunt Hanna hasn't had a bite today."

"So why don't the ninnies speak up?" Abram growls as his nervous hands wrap a sheet of cloth around his midriff into lowered trousers. But at the same time he considers: after all, the "ninnies" do take care of his merchandise. Cost an arm and a leg to get a stranger to do it. Stranger'd steal the stuff altogether. Anyone who still has a piece of bread to keep him going wouldn't take a chance on having any hot goods around. And anyone who is that hungry, no matter how lily white, can't be trusted with the stuff. Because who could pass up the temptation of such top-quality goods and let himself starve to death? Would he be any better? At

34

which court could they sue him? He'd be crazy not to do it. So Abram hastily pulls a few marks from his pocket, thrusts them into Hanna's hand, grabs Benyek by the sleeve and makes for the door: "Customer's waiting . . ."

In the window, the panes were suddenly blue. How came it she didn't notice the change? She hadn't taken her eyes off the window. Any other day by this time, she'd long since be sitting in the rag room. There you have no time to look at the window. Sunrise doesn't interest you. Daylight doesn't drive the gloom out of your heart.

The snow now falls whiter and denser. A solitary snowflake flutters furiously just outside the window pane, as though wanting to tear away from the snow multitude falling without end to the ground. All at once, the snowfall looks like a multitude being herded to the trains during an Aktion, and the snowflake as though it were pleading for the window to be opened, to be let in to hide. Finally, it falls prostrate against the pane, melts into a waterdrop and trickles down like a tear out of an open blue eye.

From the nearby corner, the porcelain tiles of the high stove stare at the window with white, frigid eyes. She doesn't recall the stove ever having been lit. Inside the stove is probably hollow. It would make a wonderful hideaway during an Aktion if you could crawl into it. It would never occur to the Germans to look there. Pity Heller didn't think of making a secret door behind the stove when he built the house. If he had, he'd still own at least one thing—a good bunker.[1] Mrs. Heller never stops harping about her tenants, who, she grumbles, are all doing a flourishing war business, but never remember to pay a few marks' rent. A pretty pass! Anything goes! But just who it is that's doing all this "war profiteering," no one knows. Out of her lovely six-room apartment and its elaborate furnishing, Mrs. Heller wanted to save at least the bookcase, the only memento of her two sons. The militiamen hurled the case full of books out of the window. You can put up a whole family where the bookcase is standing, they said. The books fluttered open in the wind and plummeted like shot birds down to the mud. Later, Shlamek gathered the books and laid them out on the ground so that his father shouldn't lie in the mud. No one would come out to the court to help carry in the Jew with JUDE seared on his brow. Everyone was afraid: the man is very

[1] Bunker: hideaway.

35

sick—needs a bed—Who wants to give his bed away in the winter and sleep on the cold floor? After all, what does a man have he can call his own these days besides the bed they're letting him sleep in—for a while? . . . Meanwhile, the blood ran from the letters JUDE, and no one would help. "Shlamek, take care of Mama . . ." Shlamek must be trekking about the ghetto backyards by now scavenging for pieces of wood, stealing chunks from thrown-out furniture, taking the loaded sack on his frail, childish shoulders, and selling the wood for kindling to the ghetto rich. His mother lies sick in bed. Ought to visit her. Perhaps bring her something she needs. The moment the curfew is off, Shlamek tears out through the gate to get to the courts ahead of his competitors. Why doesn't he chop up the rest of Mrs. Heller's bookcase? Probably hasn't the gall to do it right under her eyes. All day long Mrs. Heller sits at her window watching this last relic of her two sons. Everyone had grabbed for the cast-off books. Everyone had books for kindling that day: thick novels; gold-backed scientific and scholarly works. Somewhere in the world right now, authors are probably still writing new books. Then the books will be thrown out of the window and a youngster will lay them out in the mud under his father's back.

The Oswiencim girl crawls out of her bed, remains standing in her nightgown, stares at the tile stove as if it were the first time she were lifting her head that high. Suddenly, she jerks around, bends swiftly down, snatches the dilapidated man's shoe little Bella is playing with on the floor, dashes to the corner by the door, slides down to the floor and hides the shoe behind her back like a valuable treasure.

The infant lets out a wail. Hayim-Idl jumps up from the chest and scoops the tot into his arms. Bella is in a paroxysm of tears and Hayim-Idl doesn't know what has suddenly gone wrong. No one speaks. Tzivia doesn't say a word. Hayim-Idl rocks the infant in his arms. The baby is his whole life. Several days ago he went tearing among the beds like a maniac, hugging Bella in his arms. Daniella could never imagine Hayim-Idl looking like a wild animal. "Piss on the free world! Piss on it I say!" he ranted over and over. Heller the landlord, who likes to drop in during curfew to chat politics with Hayim-Idl, had happened to remark, "After the war there will be a free world . . ." "What's the good of a free world," Hayim-Idl railed, "if I won't be around and my baby won't be around? Piss on the free world! The devil take a free world that asks for the blood of my Bella!"

Bella doesn't stop crying in her father's arms and Hayim-Idl doesn't know how to pacify her. In the corner by the door, the Oswiencim girl draws the shoe from behind her back, hugs it to her heart and, sitting on the floor, offers it to Hayim-Idl with a trembling hand, as if letting go a dearest possession. The infant looks at the shoe as at a fascinating doll, and immediately stops crying.

"You're all right," Hayim-Idl says to the Oswiencim girl. The girl lowers her head and murmurs into her upraised knees, "Don't want . . ."

The girl brought this shoe along when she fled here, after the Germans had cleaned all the Jews out of Oswiencim to make way for their concentration camp "Auschwitz." She's about fourteen or fifteen years old. Maybe much older, or maybe much younger. It's hard to say. Sometimes she looks like a child, sometimes like an old woman. No telling when and how her face will next transmute right before your eyes. Some kind of quirk. When she first got here, the neighbours sometimes would give her a piece of bread, a potato. All because of her capricious face. Even the militiamen were moved when they saw the comic-repugnant fickleness of her face, and quartered her in the Centre—and no ransom asked. She never says a word, and her eyes are always downcast. When asked anything, she raises her eyes no higher than the questioner's feet, and simpers, "Don't want . . ." There hasn't been an Aktion in the ghetto that she hasn't fore-sensed. As if she had had advance notice from the Gestapo High Command. She always vanishes before an Aktion, and manages to find herself hideouts no one else would ever dream of. She furtively steals out of the Centre and as furtively steals back in when the trouble is over. With the same instinct by which a jungle beast senses the enemy's approach from miles away, she always seems to scent the Germans in advance. Not a single Jew in Oswiencim was saved. Not one of her family survived. No one knows what her eyes beheld there. She simply slipped in here one midnight with the dilapidated man's shoe in her hand.

What secret does this man's shoe contain that the girl hugs it so to her heart?

Outside, the snow falls white and dense. Hanna stands facing the window, praying out of the prayer book in her

37

hand. Tzivia continues to sit on the bed, her head cupped in one hand, the other propped on the bedpost. Her eyes are fixed pensively on her sister's back. Hayim-Idl is back at his goods, putting them from the chest on the floor, and from the floor again into the chest.

. . . Why not just go up to Hayim-Idl and ask him if he has any work for her? What's all this bashfulness? No question, if he had anything, he'd have told her. Maybe she should beg him for it. But what good will her begging do if he hasn't anything? He'll just have to turn her down. All it will do is make him feel sorry for her. "Feel sorry." Why call it "feel sorry"? The airs of a proud pauper! *"Proud pauper . . ."* Such familiar words! Where has she seen or heard them before? The swan! She herself used these words in describing the swan: "*. . . she plunges her noble bill deep, deep into the water, doesn't chew—lest she be suspected of beggary—but gracefully swallows her prey, and goes sailing majestically back across her mirror-lake—a proud pauper. . . .*"

Daniella sat on her bed, hands rammed deep in her coat pockets. The room and everything in it was crammed in her eyes. Suddenly she felt she was seeing it all for the first time; as if a moment ago she hadn't been here. Everything seemed so glaringly strange and new: the walls, the snow falling outside, the open chest in Hayim-Idl's "villa," the girl in the long nightgown sitting on the floor by the door—what does it all mean? It must be a dream. Any moment now and she'll hear Pa's gay whistle waking her to go to school. She'll open her eyes and there he'll be, like every morning, in the doorway of her room, his blue eyes smiling at her, the spotless towel slung around his neck, ready to take over the bathroom. Of course it's a dream . . . Everything around her now can't be more than a bad dream. Just like the nightmare where she saw herself running toward the swans. The fright of that nightmare is still there as real as ever. That time she was also positive she was really seeing it all happen. She can still see the faces of those train guards. She sees them as clearly as she sees Hanna there near the window, holding the prayer book in her hands. . . . Harry bound within the cloud . . . A white cloud like the white snow falling outside. Harry gapes at her with petrified eyes. She stil! feels the horror that had racked her during that dream: they're after her. Bells clang and they're chasing her! Now she knows it was only the night tram clanging through the street. And when she comes out of this dream, maybe then she'll understand why she—

The door flew open. Fella breezed into the room. A round loaf of bread was tucked under her arm. Her coat was snow-specked. She chucked the bread on to her bed and started shaking her flossy black curls like a handsome filly tossing its mane. The melted snowdrops spattered in all directions. "Wow! I wouldn't send a dog of a Judenrat man out in this weather," Fella sallies, taking off her flashy coat and spreading it over her bedpost to dry. The room, until a moment ago stale and dreary, now perked up at the breath of life that came in with Fella. "Hey, folks" she banters, "the bread isn't walking into your pretty mouths. What you waiting for? Want me to spoon-feed you like Dvortche spoon-feeds her Bella?"

Hayim-Idl gets up from the chest, reaches into his "kitchen" for a knife, and goes over to Fella. "You know, Fella, if you don't cut up the bread and hand it to them, they'll just sit there like wall-flowers waiting to be asked. Looks like they're used to having their mamas spoon-feed them."

Fella rolls her wet silk stockings off her shapely legs, hurls them under the bed like so much rubbish, and turns her head to the window.

"Hanna! God's in the middle of an awful spat with his wife. He's so mad, He ripped his quilt to pieces. Can't you see the feathers flying all over the place? Why don't you leave him be? He doesn't give a hoot about your prayers right now, anyway!"

Hanna's shoulder flinches, as if wanting to shake off Fella's blasphemy. She goes on praying inaudibly from the prayer book in her hands, only her lips moving.

"Shut your trap, Fella, or I'll shut it for you!" Hayim-Idl's voice booms out of the chest like out of a deep, hollow barrel.

"Go to bed, saint!"

"Never you mind, Hayim-Iddie. God's laying out a nice free world for you. Better tell your Dvortche to get a juicy hot stew ready for the big day."

"Enough out of you," he bellows into the chest. "Better give your mouth a good rinsing before saying The-Name-I-Daren't-Mention. It's you and the likes of you that we're all suffering for!"

Fella cuts the bread, tosses slice after slice to all the beds. "If that's the way it is," she retorts, "if it's me the Jews are suffering for, then I'd better hit the hay. Nighty night, Hayim-Iddie! Nighty night, lovely free world!"

"Good night, good night! Pleasant dreams!" Hayim-Idl flashes back. "Maybe you'd like me to sing you a lullaby?"

Fella pulls the blanket over her head, parrying toward Hayim-Idl: "Take it from me, Hayim-Idl, your own little Bella could use a lullaby much better. If there's a God in heaven, He sure knows it! I'll sing me my own lullaby. Don't go putting yourself out for me." She curls up snugly inside the blanket, and her voice comes crooning from under it:

> "Pretty girlies get kissed,
> Ugly ducklings are hissed . . . ."

Fella is a beautiful, svelte brunette of about twenty, with twin rows of sparkling, laughing teeth. She was hardly along in her teens when men were already flocking around her. Fella knew all the ins and outs of the male heart. She knew how to wrap them around her finger and how to make them keep their distance. All in all, she showed them which was the "weaker sex."

But Fella made her biggest conquest while working as a waitress in the most fashionable saloon in her home town, Radno. The young Polish postmaster, Yeszy, fell in love with her and spent half his nights in the saloon just to be near her. He was ready to give his right arm for a smile from Fella. But Fella didn't want his right arm, and did not give him a smile. Men were an open book to Fella. The university of Radno-saloon was second to none in the world.

During the Jew liquidation at Radno, Fella escaped to Yeszy's apartment. Yeszy was in the seventh heaven. It didn't matter to him that Fella had come to him only to hide. He only knew that Fella was in his house, and that was all he cared about. But no sooner did the Germans post signs on all the house walls, "Death to any Pole hiding a Jew!" than Yeszy ordered her to leave. Can't she see she can no longer stay in his house? He said it in all simplicity, as if it were an obvious thing. Fella eyed him, said nothing. What was there for her to say? Yeszy wanted her to understand his position—and she understood. She's no baby. Of course she understands. Just one thing: Would Yeszy, who

40

used to be ready to give his right arm for her smile, allow her to stay until dark? That evening, when Yeszy, like all the Christians in Radno, placed in the window an icon of the Holy Mother over a burning kerosene lamp, as a sign that a pure Aryan lived there, Fella quietly opened the door and slipped out without a word. She slunk her way through the Jew-less streets and across the fields to an old acquaintance of hers—a militiaman in Jew-Quarter 3.

Now Fella snaps her fingers at the world. "Life doesn't rate even one little tear from a girl like me!" she maintains. Every evening she goes to make a night of it at militia headquarters. Mornings she returns to the Centre with a loaf of bread under her arm. Not for herself. Fella doesn't need any bread. Sometimes she also brings a whole package of margarine. She gives it out with all her heart, with laughing teeth. Even the two God-fearing girls help themselves to Fella's bread. If they knew what price she was paying for the bread, they might not want to touch it. But the two of them are still living in their own sinless world, with not an evil thought to cross their minds.

Occasionally Fella brings home a pair of sheer silk stockings. She draws them up her lovely legs, admires the exquisite arcs extended before her, sizing them up as a commander reviewing his troops presenting their gleaming bayonets. Convinced that her weapons will pass, she slams them down to the floor and starts whistling a merry hit tune. Daniella can help herself to her old stockings if she feels like it. Or anybody else for that matter. It's all the same to Fella. Lots more where these came from. For all she cares they can rot under the bed. Fella isn't forcing anyone, Fella isn't begging anyone. She's just a good kid. Just one thing: how about letting her get some sleep now? She hasn't had a wink all night. They really went to town at the militia last night, and the bastards didn't lay off her all night. Didn't even let her catch her breath.

4

THEY sat on the stone steps of the Judenrat soup kitchen.

Harry's clothes were soaked through and through with wet snow from the long trek through the fields. He fumbled at his coat buttons but couldn't get them open. As though it were something too hard to do. His hands were wet, numb from the icy wind. He felt as though his fingers were swathed in bandages.

"It's murder, this winter," he said.

The snow on his hat was melting. She saw the water trickle, drop, drop off the faded, rumpled hat brim on to his back and shoulders, and immediately be sponged up in the wetness of his coat. She wanted to take the hat off his head, but didn't. Her hands wouldn't stretch out.

Harry turned back the flap of his coat and with both hands tried to pull a paper-wrapped parcel out of his pocket. Daniella watched his efforts with wide, mute eyes and it didn't occur to her that she could help him. It wouldn't have been any trouble for her to pull such a parcel out of the side pocket of his trousers. She was like one just coming out of a coma, whose mind is still in a fog.

. . . Always, before Harry comes, she has a thousand things to tell him. But the moment she sees him, she suddenly seems to lose her tongue. The words sink somewhere deep inside her, and something altogether different wells up in their place. Waves, waves sweep over her heart toward her throat and clog there together with her breath. She forgets all the thousands of things she wanted to tell him. She feels like a bottle filled to the cork—full, but looking empty.

The bread which Harry pulled out of his pockets was sodden with the rain that had drenched him down to the trouser pocket. The dark marmalade showed between the two oval crusts of bread. He peeled the soggy paper off one end of the sandwich and offered it to her.

"Eat, Dani," he said.

She looked at his outstretched hands. They were gnarled and wet, trembling like an old man's. She hastily took the bread from him, turned her face away, and with both hands held the bread to her closed lips.

Always, whenever she thinks of him, she pictures him the way he used to look: handsome, elegant, cutting a very impressive figure. Even while waiting for him near the fields, when she talks to him in her thoughts, she sees him no differently. She can't picture Harry looking any other way. She forgets. She always forgets. She is so excited—she's going to see him in a little while. But the moment she sees him, her knees begin to tremble. She is panic-stricken: she

42

doesn't recognize the face. It takes some time before she accustoms herself again to the fact that this is Harry.

Outside, the moist snow was still falling. Harry sat beside her. He looked out to the soup kitchen compound, not saying anything, as if he wanted to avoid disturbing her while she ate. The wooden fence around the compound and the two stark trees near it seemed from afar like a pencil sketch drawn by kindergarten children on grey cardboard. Every now and then wives of Judenrat officials rushed by the corridor entrance, carrying loaded baskets, sealed or well covered with a blanket to hide their contents from hungry eyes. Once this building was a Jewish school. Now it is the Judenrat supply depot. Hundreds of people could have been housed here. But the Judenrat doesn't want anyone to see what is going on here.

Harry was looking out to the compound. "The marmalade should taste good. Sanya kept it for you all week. This morning it didn't seem I'd be able to make it. It's murder, this winter. Good thing it's almost over."

Slowly she raised her eyes to his profile. She felt as though pincers were clamping her throat. She searched the face for some trace of what it had looked like, but couldn't find it. As though the old Harry had been burned to an ash within this frame, with the pain still smouldering around his head. *"It's murder, this winter."* Wintertime, whenever Harry came home to visit, they would both go ice-skating together. No one else performed such figures on the ice. Everybody watched him with admiration and she would be so proud of him. She used to wish that winter would last for ever, that it should never never end and that Harry should be home, always.

At the window where the free soup was being distributed, the cries reached the high heavens. There hunger was ruthlessly kneading a gigantic human mass. Dishevelled heads, hands clutching pots overhead, women howling for mercy. The human dough heaved and tossed, interkneading with the falling wet snow. Each was afraid that when his turn came the window would slam shut in his face: No more soup! Women screamed piteously out of the mob: They're being crushed! Men rammed elbows into hearts of feebler ones, cutting themselves a path to the window. The militiamen stood by to make sure that only those who had first turned

43

in their ration coupons reached the window. The rest didn't concern them.

Every time the Gestapo demands a transport load of Jews, the Judenrat helps itself first to those who live off the soup kitchen. Everyone knows where the transports are taken. Nevertheless, the compound is always jammed with people. They disregard what will happen to them afterwards. They only know that now they can make for the soup kitchen with an empty pot and bring home some warm soup for the children.

Harry muses: Ferber is now with the Rabbi of Shiliv, still trying to convince him that they are all going to die and that the only way for them to glorify God is by revolting as one man against the Germans. Good idea for Ferber to come to the compound. Here he would see how people "glorify"— for a plate of warm soup. Glorify God! What is it worth? Who will volunteer to go and get killed if there's not even a spoonful of soup in it? Who'll pay attention to him? These people in the compound—they certainly won't. And if they don't, who will? Even Sanya, intelligent and wise as she is, doesn't see eye to eye with Ferber. And he himself, is his mind all made up about it? Could he agree to something which would mean certain death for Sanya and Daniella? Tedek. Clear-minded Tedek. The hundred-per-cent man. That steel will in the eyes. Just one glance at him told you that here was a man who knows what he wants and that he would get there. Sanya had argued, "Tedek is going out to certain death." And Ferber retorted, "A dead man can't go out to his death." And what was the outcome? Whom did his disappearance benefit? An hour before he went out of the ghetto, Tedek said, "I'm leaving the ghetto not as a dead man, nor as one heading for death. I'm leaving the ghetto because I'm alive and am going to bring life to others! My going will pave the way for all of you." Won't everyone be going in Tedek's "paved way"? Then Ferber must be right. But couldn't Tedek still be here now, together with us? Then Sanya is right! Where does this lean red-headed Ferber get this drive burning in him day and night? Where does he get this tenacity and courage? Can he win over the Rabbi of Shiliv?

Through the compound gate comes a dilapidated wicker baby carriage on tall, spindly wheels. An old man sits in it, and two youngsters—a boy and a girl—wheel it along. The

44

boy pulls the carriage with a rope in front, and the girl pushes it with her hands from behind. The old man's knees are raised level with his head, their angles jutting from the baby carriage. In the crook of his stomach, between his knees and head, sits a big, sooty pot. The snow falls mercilessly on the carriage, on the old man's scraggly, grizzly-green beard, on the raw, peeled-down lower lids of his bleary eyes. He doesn't budge, as if it does not bother him at all, the way it doesn't bother the bare tree-stump there by the fence. The children wheel the carriage up to the window, where they have to turn in the ration coupons. The boy goes up to the old man, undoes the coat button over his chest, and pulls out the soggy ration card. The old man doesn't stir. He stares blankly with the red-fleshed lower lids of his dripping eyes at the wet stone wall of the soup-kitchen building.

. . . Harry was never this quiet. There was so much she was going to tell him before he came, and now she feels as though her throat were clogged. It would feel so good if she could only cry herself out on his shoulder. But that would only make it harder on him. Never has he been this quiet. He always had so much to talk about, and how she loved listening and telling him of her own thoughts and feelings! He probably doesn't touch a piece of bread all week. You can't even get a loaf of bread at the black market on the monthly wages of the shop. Who collects the miserable salary, anyway? Everyone is afraid. They all want to broadcast their patriotism to the Germans, their readiness to give up the salary for the cause. Harry probably doesn't take his wages at Schwecher's either. He wouldn't want to be the only one. She at least makes something once in a while. She's much better off than he. He'd have been terribly hurt if she hadn't taken the bread. She knows it. If he only knew that she can't swallow the bite down, that she chokes on his bread. But she knows that he wants so much for her to eat. How can she tell him how awfully drawn his face looks? That he needs the bread much more than she? *"Sanya kept the marmalade for you all week."* Who knows how long they've been saving the two crusts just so Harry could bring them along today? When Sanya used to visit them in Kongressia, the whole house would tingle with her impish gaiety. In those days she didn't really know Sanya. She was such a baby then. But she should have known even then that if Harry had chosen Sanya for a wife, she must be more than just a pretty flirt

45

showing off stylish suits. Everybody used to stop and stare at her on the street. "A Paris model . . ." they would buzz. It's been a long time since she last saw Sanya . . .

"How is Sanya?" The question slipped out unexpectedly. She was surprised herself to hear the words come from her mouth.

"Sanya is doing all she can to get the Judenrat to let you live with us. It's almost all set. But there's still the problem of getting you placed in a shop."

Deep down Daniella knows that she would never agree to it. If she lives with Harry he'll have to feed her too. Harry will never allow her to smuggle goods under her coat, which means she won't be able to pay her way any more and will be taking away his last bite. No. Never. Harry wants to throw everything over for her sake. Sanya will never be able to get the red Gestapo stamp for her. Silly. You don't just get such things. All that will happen is that they'll catch her in Harry's place, and all three of them will be sent off to Auschwitz. Harry has become so reckless . . .

"Too bad all the trouble Sanya's going to," she said.

"Why, Dani? Maybe you and Sanya will even work together in the same shop."

"I'll never agree to such a thing."

He swung around to look at her:

"You, Daniella, will do as I tell you! Sanya knows what she's doing!"

The harsh tone of Harry's words was sweet to her ears, although she knew that in this case she would never obey him. The firmness of his voice warmed her heart with love and gratitude. Like a mother at the sick-bed of her child too weak to talk, suddenly hearing him complain violently.

When Harry turned to look at her, he saw her still holding the bread to her lips, untouched.

"Why don't you eat, Dani?" he asked softly.

She looked to him. Their glances linked.

"I'll eat it there, in the Centre," she said.

He put his arm around her shoulder and she nestled her head on his heart. The cold wetness of his coat was near and dear to her as part of him. She felt hot streams washing over her heart, rushing into the throat, the eyes. She felt the touch of his hand on her hair. She felt she must hurry and say something. But there was nothing she could say. There wasn't a word in the world that could solace him and her; a word that would make up for the wetness of his coat, the fields he'll soon have to splash through, and all that's happening around them here in the soup-kitchen compound. She wanted to cry.

"Harrik," she said, "you were never this quiet."

He stroked her head. Outside, the sky hung dank and bleak over the compound. The house they were sitting in was like an ark carried along on a flood, and the trees in the distance like the outstretched arms of drowners. At the soup window, three children supported their swooning mother whom they had dragged out of the mob. The woman didn't have the strength to walk by herself. Her own limbs were too much for her to lift, but her clamped fingers wouldn't let go of the empty pot. The children led her away, and wailing "Mama! Mama!" they brought her to the wall of the building. No one turned to look at them. The rain poured angrily, mixed with wet, sticky snowflakes. No one paid attention to them.

Harry gently caressed her head. He was looking outside. The words rang in his ears. "*You were never this quiet . . .*"

"What's there to say, Dani?" he said.

She raised her head to him:

"You know, Harrik, sometimes it seems that all this is only a dream. Sometimes I feel I'm going to wake up and find it was just a horrid nightmare. You'll again come home from Warsaw with the pretty tan suitcase in your hand and the travelling coat over your arm. Once more we'll just get up and walk anywhere we feel like. No more Jew-Quarters. You'll wait for me near school, come up and doff your hat with a deep bow. Remember? . . . But don't forget to say: 'May I have the pleasure of the mademoiselle's company for a brief afternoon promenade?' Remember to say, Harrik— to say . . ."

The words came out spasmodically. A stifled weeping writhed in her throat. He drew her to him.

"Dani, Dani," he soothed, "of course it's only a dream. It's all a dream—a passing dream."

She looked at him with wide, dazed eyes. "No, Harrik. This isn't a dream." Her fingers fluttered over his face, groped along the protruding bones of his sunken cheeks. "No, Harrik, this is not a dream—Oh, Harrik."

He pressed her head to his chest. Her shoulders heaved as

she wept. He didn't know how to calm her. She herself wanted to calm down, but couldn't.

An excited man huffed into the corridor where they sat, holding with both hands a steaming pot of soup. The steam rose from the pot toward his agitated face. He sat himself in a corner near the wall, as though hiding from someone, or as if he couldn't spare the few additional steps to the staircase, where he would be able to sit and eat unmolested. He held the pot close to his mouth, and with a tin spoon kept baling the soup into his mouth without pause, without stopping for a breath. Sweat and melted snowflakes streamed down his flushed face into the pot. He didn't interrupt his meal even to wipe the rivulets of sweat and water from his brow.

A little girl of about six stopped at the corridor entrance. She had finally found her father and remained standing there, looking at him, as if afraid to get too near him. The rain was dripping from her scrubby braids. She was wrapped in a large, patched man's jacket girded with a piece of string. The oversize sleeves were rolled up the scrawny little arms. Silently she gazed up at her father's open mouth and at the spoonfuls of hot soup continually disappearing into it.

Daniella embraced Harry's hands between her palms. She looked at them with lowered head as she spoke. "Shameless me. You risk your life every Sunday to come to me and all I do is blubber at you. I'm no good."

"What's this you're saying about my goldilocks? You are my own golden Dani! My lovely blossom—"

"You always called me your lovely blossom, Harrik. Remember?"

"Of course you're my lovely blossom. Of course I said so."

"You know, Harrik, always before you come, I have a million things I want to tell you. But the moment we're sitting together, I forget. I always forget. Only later I remember, when you're gone. What a pig I am. Why did I have to cry?"

"When the heart runs over, we cry. What other relief do we have these days?"

"You always were wonderful. Mummy always loved you more than me."

"That's not so. My, but aren't you still the jealous little cat!"

"Harrik," she suddenly strung out his name very earnestly, "I have something to tell you."

"Aha, there goes my little blabbermouth. What is it this time?"

"First promise to keep it for ever between us."

"All right, if that's what you want. I promise."

"No!" She gripped his hand as in a handshake. "Only if you shake on it!"

"Piggyhead! Who doesn't know Dani the piggyhead? All right! I'll shake. Your hand's so warm!"

"Not 'all right'! 'Honest to goodness'!"

" 'Honest to goodness'! Am I going to hear it before curfew time? ..."

"You know, Harrik, back in Kongressia, I didn't especially care for Sanya. But that was then. Today I love her more than I love you—you promised! Remember!"

Harry put on a grave face, as if he had just heard some news of great importance. Secretly he was glad to see Daniella transformed before his eyes back into the child she really was. He knew how desperately she needed a father's caress, a mother's embrace. Her spirit thirsted for it like a parched plant for a drop of dew. He was happy that he had been able to distract her for a little while as one distracts a child. He pulled himself together and continued, "Now you'll admit you've always been a jealous little cat. Confess now—isn't it so?"

She nodded poutingly.

The man in the corner had finished the soup in the pot. He licked the spoon clean on both sides, shoved it into his breast pocket and turned to leave the corridor. The little girl stepped out of his way. He passed by her as if he did not see her. She turned around and dumbly followed him out.

After a few steps outside, the father swung his head around to the tagging child—as though he had only just noticed her —scowled at her, and like a preoccupied person trying to brush an annoying fly off his nose, he hissed through his teeth: "Die!"

And walked on.

The girl stood there. She was afraid to move a step forward lest she get too near her father. "*Die!*" The ground-out curse from between his teeth was well known and frightened her more than the hunger in her stomach. The wind whipped

49

her face with lashes of wet snow. She did not weep. She was just very lonely.

The father was darting ferrety glances, now towards the militiamen on duty, now at the soup window. It was obvious he was scheming how to cut back into the throng without the militiamen noticing. Once lost in the mob, he'd know what to do. The main thing, to get by the militiamen.

"You really think there's no hope of getting word from Pa and Ma?" Daniella suddenly asked. "Zalke promised that if he manages to get back to Metropoli again, he'll try to bring a letter from them and leave it for me with Leon the gold dealer. I have to stop in there every so often to check if there is anything."

Harry mused. With the snake pit proper, with Berlin, he had managed to make contact. He even talked to Berlin by phone. But to Kongressia ghetto, the realm of a Jewish "king," there is no getting through. As if the ghetto were immured in steel.

"Don't you dare go to the gold dealer!" he admonished. "The Germans might pull a search just when you happen to be there. They'll be looking for gold, and they'll find you. I'll think of some other way of contacting Kongressia. I've had a promise about that."

Like welded links of a chain, image after image flashed through her mind: Zalke, the bread full of diamonds and dollar bills, the Russian "porker" the seam ripper found under the patched knee of the overalls, Schultze, the German supervisor, the arrival of the Germans in Yablova, her father's face fading into the station, Moni, "*Dani, why are you going away?*"

All at once she said, "Helier the landlord says the war won't last much longer. Want to see Moni?"

She unbuttoned her coat and drew out the locket hanging on her breast. She leaned closer to Harry. Their heads touched. The innocent, cherubic face of their little brother gazed at them from Daniella's palm with velvety astonishment. They could hear him calling them by name.

"Moni would be nine now," she said.

Harry took the locket in his hand, turned it over. There, his father's face looked up at him with deep blue eyes—the very eyes he and Daniella inherited from him—and by his father's head the gentle face of his mother, the face he loved and worshipped above all in the world.

Under the balcony, near the house wall, the woman sat on the ground in frozen posture. The rain cascaded and swept a tuft of hair down her face. It was hard to make out whether she was alive at all, in a swoon, or just staring with stony eyes at the three children scampering about her, their little heads huddled between emaciated shoulders because of the downpour, and taking turns wailing, "Mama! Mama!"

The sweep of hair on the woman's face gave Harry no rest. Where and when had he seen this woman before? When was there a similar downpour in which he had seen her with the self-same rainswept tuft of hair? The riddle burrowed in his mind the way you sometimes forget a simple expression, the name of a familiar, everyday thing: you can see it in your mind, almost touch it with your tongue, but you just can't nudge it out to your lips. He remembers it was just this kind of downpour. He sees the tuft of hair against the backdrop of a downpour. Seems he even saw the children. But where, when? . . .

Daniella was looking at the picture in the locket, sunk in thought. Outside, the snow fell denser and crisper. In the centre of the compound the baby carriage was still standing, with the old man in it in the same pose as before. The big empty pot on his stomach suddenly looked like an intricately wrought ashtray welded to the midriff of a classic mythological figure.

Suddenly it struck him. The picture flashed into his mind in clear focus. He remembered: of course, the woman with the sweep of hair on her face!

It was after a major Aktion in the ghetto. He had hurried to find out about Daniella. At the train the Germans were already loading the captives into the cars, while in the ghetto the first hiders were scuttling out of the holes—some to avoid asphyxiation, some to find out who of their family had been taken. They scurried about helter-skelter, their eyes wild with terror: though the captives are already being loaded into the trains, the Germans are liable to return to the ghetto if they find there is some room to spare in the cars, and pick up whomever they come across. The hole looked as if it had been dug with frantic hands and hastily covered over with branches. The woman crawled out of the earth as from a grave. The gritty tuft of hair was dangling down her face. She stood on top of a mound, eyes glaring down toward the railway lines. As the trains started pulling out, she clapped

51

her hands and murmured fervently, "Praise the Lord they're finally being taken! Praise the Lord they're finally being taken! . . ."

She didn't stop clapping her hands and praising God.

In the hole, the children lay curled like worms in the subsoil. The same strand of hair. Downpour.

But it wasn't a downpour of water; it was a downpour of fire and fury, God's wrath.

At the window, soup distribution was over. The sky sagged wet and grey on to the compound. The huge mass of people, who but a moment ago had filled the world with their clamour, now crumbled like a dried-up dough. Each to himself. As if the paste which had previously held them together had suddenly dried up. The people trailed off, bowed, silent, each his way. Beaten minikins. Empty pots. Faded into the wet greyness between sky and earth. Only the baby carriage with the old man in it remained standing in the centre of the compound, like a rare art object in a large museum hall set aside especially for it.

Harry stood up. He went over to the corridor entrance. Outside, it looked as if the world had condensed into a dank, grey mist. He couldn't see the fields or the mountains on the way to Jew-Quarter 1.

'Almost curfew time," he said. "Sanya will be worried."

Daniella went up to him. The whole while she'd been waiting to tell him this, but could not bring herself to it. She kept pushing it off to the last moment.

"Harry, promise you won't come through the fields any more. Not until you have a transit pass. You're taking your life in your hands. I can't understand how Sanya allows it."

Harry suddenly remembered.

"Oh, yes, I meant to tell you. I might be put on night shift. I don't know when I'll be able to come again. Night-shift workers hardly ever get Sundays off."

Her heart twinged. He won't be coming any more! She tried with all her might not to show what she felt. Just a moment ago she had asked him not to come. She had insisted on it.

"It's terrible, working at night," she said.

Harry buttoned his coat all the way up. For the thousandth time he now wondered: He always meets his quota. Why does Poldek the supervisor pick on him? Of all the machine operators in the tailor shop he picks him for the night shift!

What did he do to Poldek that he suddenly started going after him so sadistically? He sits there in the corner at his machine all day, minding his own business. He was always sure nobody notices him; that Poldek doesn't see him, or watch him, let alone know him. Why did Poldek pick on him?

"It's not as terrible as it seems," he said. "Nothing is terrible any more, Dani. It only hurts me that I won't be able to see you as often as before. Don't let it upset you, Dani. Sanya's bound to get your transfer through."

He embraced her head and drew her eyes to his lips. "I've got to run," he said.

Daniella quickly undid her coat and stripped off her sweater.

"Take it, Harry," she said.

"Not for the world! What an idea!"

"You put that sweater on this minute! I have my raincoat and you still have such a long way ahead of you! Put it on this instant, you scamp!"

"Piggyhead! Who doesn't know Dani the piggyhead?"

She forced his coat off. It was wet and heavy with water. She pulled the sweater over his head. His body was all skin and bones. The sweater seemed terribly big on him. She clenched her teeth to suppress a scream.

She stood at the edge of the compound watching him fade out of sight. From time to time he turned his head to her. From the distance he looked like an old, derelict vagabond, drifting along the bleak byways of the world. Before disappearing behind the first mountain he halted for the last time, swung around to her, and with a deep flourish doffed his hat to her from afar.

The scene flashed before her eyes and tore daggers at her heart—

"*May I have the pleasure of mademoiselle's company for a brief afternoon promenade? . . .*"

5

WINTER passed, summer came. No one even noticed it. In the ghetto they had long forgotten to notice such things. The sun does not dry tears, as the poets have it. For they kept flowing ever fresh as from a well which, it seemed, would never run dry. In the ghetto streets no children played. In the ghetto there were no children. There were small Jews and there were big Jews—all looking alike. The children wore on their little sleeves the same Jew armband as the elders. Just as with the yellow patch sewn against the heart. Dvortche, Hayim-Idl's wife, embroidered a tiny yellow hexagram, like a Star of David, and sewed it to Bella's dress over the heart. "How sweet! How charming!" Hayim-Idl couldn't stop rhapsodizing. And the tiny patch really had poignant charm, like the first wee white shoes of an infant.

That still another summer was passing, nobody in the shoe shop noticed. But everyone did notice that the canteen man had got himself a new partner. The turnover in the canteen in the shoe shop attic grew by leaps and bounds. Lately the canteen has branched out like a secret holding company, with invisible shareholders somewhere outside the shop walls.

Originally, the semi-dark attic was just a cloakroom. The canteen man handed out checks and took care of the shop workers' clothes. At the same time, he also carried a sweetish soda of sorts. What else was available in the ghetto? Even this cloying drink was a luxury only the rich "screwturners" could afford. By now the canteen has become a big operation. There you can get the choicest dishes: roast goose, cheese-cake, beer, and potassium cyanide.

The choicest—cyanide.

In a corner of the attic, behind the door, stands a man with a sphinx-like expression, hand buried in his trouser pocket. With him there is no talk. With him the transaction is carried out wordlessly. Just with the eyes. The incomer extends a tremulous hand. Not raising it, but holding it by his thigh, palm up, he extends quavery fingers. One pair of eyes asks:

"Sure it's all there?"

The second pair of eyes replies:

"Yes."

"You're not holding out on me?"

Sphinxface in the dark corner puts a reassuring hand on the doubter's shoulder, pats him lightly, intimately, and sends him off, stating with his eyes, "Relax. It's all there. . . ."

After this mute spiritualistic rite, the cobbler is ready to go ahead and eat cheese-cake.

A cheese-cake industry. Where do they get such cheese-cake nowadays? Cobblers didn't set such cheese-cake on their table even before the war!

From the darkness behind the coat-hangers, the canteen man's head keeps materializing out of the floor like an apparition, dispensing slices of cheese-cake. One of the partners stands on the margin between the dark and light, whispering continuously at the floor:

"Quarter."

"Bubbler."

"Goo."

The canteen man sprawls somewhere on the floor, weighing slices of cake, ripping chunks of roast goose, uncapping beer bottles—and dispensing. There is so much to be done. The customers are in line waiting their turn. He doesn't let out a sound. He just dispenses. Here's the quarter—a quarter of roast goose; here's the bubbler—a tall glass of foaming beer; and here's the goo—a half-pound slice of cheese-cake. All without a word. Hands reach out of the dark and serve to the heart's desire. The cheese-cake pans are concealed in the hollow between the attic floor and the machine-room ceiling. On the wooden floor lies a pile of clothes, ostensibly brought in for ripping.

A day-long pilgrimage to the attic. Those going up, those coming down. They pass each other on the stairs, not saying a word, not exchanging a glance. Each knows why the other is on his way up to the attic. By the entrance they stop and wait silently for the others to come out. Each knows why the other has come here, and why they are all standing here. So they wait in silence, like men waiting together in the foyer of a brothel.

II

When Daniella heard the terrible news, Harry was already loaded on one of the trains.

It happened during a week-end, on a beautiful summer night. The Germans swooped down on the night shift in Schwecher's tailor shop in Jew-Quarter 1, stopped the machines, and took the workers to the labour camp.

Harry was among those taken.

In the shoe shop Vevke roamed from room to room, from table to table, and just could not settle down. Work in the shoe shop was not the way it used to be. The ghetto atmosphere rushed in through the walls of the fortress called shoe-shop like the sea into a floundering vessel. Vevke wanted to go over to Daniella and console her. But when he got to the threshold of the rag room he halted. His feet wouldn't take him any further. Seeing the girl's head lowered to the garment she was ripping, the consoling word suddenly dried up inside him and he could find nothing instead to say to her now. The girl's despondent face bared the unhealed wounds in his own heart. He always felt his own pain most acutely through the pain of others. Better not go to her now. He wheeled around and went to one of the cobblers' tables, snatched a pair of "mates," with the other hand pulled a wooden sole out of the basket, and dived into work, like someone going into a tavern to drown a racking sorrow.

The news about Schwecher's shop was no longer discussed at the cobblers' tables. It was already just another one of those ghetto events, a thing of the past. But then politics, too, wasn't discussed any more—either at the high cutting-tables or at the low cobblers' tables. Gone were the sweet snatches of stolen conversation at the tables. Moreover, no one even missed them. Everyone put questions to himself that could not be discussed with others. Everyone wondered: Whose turn will it be next? When will the next Aktion strike? What will it be like? Will it again be the shops? Or a children's Aktion? Or maybe the women this time? The childless calculated that it had been a long time since the last children's Aktion, and decided it was about time for the children. Fathers of sons figured out that it would be the daughters this time. Each found that he himself was not in the category due next, and one and all were sure that after the big raid at Schwecher's the Germans would lay off the shops for at least a while. And what does one crave above all?—a little while.

One more breath, and you may be liberated.

Bergson, the cantor of the "atheists'" synagogue, looks sideways at the hammer falling rhythmically in Vevke's hand, and at the nails sprouting and vanishing so systematically into the narrow tape around the wooden sole. With himself, Bergson muses, the "mates" are always either too long or too short for the sole. Though it seems to him he's always very careful to pick out the right size "mates." Must be some unfathomable cobblers' secret. Not once did his blood freeze on seeing the last nails betray him. It's never until the last nails that the "mates" show themselves to be out of kilter. More than once has Schultze sent people to

56

Auschwitz for this kind of slip. "Wilful sabotage" he calls it. If not for Vevke he'd long since have ended up in Auschwitz. Vevke never misses the meaning of his upraised eyes, and always knows how to save the shoe. And always in the nick of time. It's beyond him: no sooner does the shoe feel Vevke's touch than the long isn't long any more and the short isn't short. Just some cobbling secret! But even Schultze has cut down on his slinking along the workroom walls lately. All told, the shoe shop now looks as in the midst of a mourning recess; the festive-mournful air of stores closed for the funeral of some great personage. It had always been so crowded at the cutting-tables, and at the cobblers' tables your arm couldn't move freely because of your neighbour's arm. Even the "screwturners" don't show up at the shop any more. "The best labour card is a good bunker," they say. And they are really setting themselves up good bunkers. Leave it to them. They know what they're about. No Aktion ever gets them. They even manage to wriggle out of the Dulag.[1]

Vevke tosses one completed shoe after another into the basket. No slowing up for him, Bergson observes. As if he meant to bolster up the tottering walls of the shoe shop with his own two shoulders. Twenty years they lived as neighbours in the same house, and in all that time he never got to know the greatness of Vevke the man. He first saw it the day the Germans drove all the Jews of their street out of their homes. They were all wailing and weeping and tearing at their hair. But Vevke—first he sent his wife and five sons on ahead. Then he took the cobblers' table on his shoulder and the tool kit in his other hand. On the threshold of the house he stopped, set the tool kit on the ground, reached his hand to the mezuzah,[2] brushed his glue-caked fingertips over it and kissed them, abruptly bent and took hold of the tool kit, and stepped from the home where he had passed more than half his life; where his children's cribs had stood; where he'd earned his bread with honest sweat; where every nook and corner was precious to him.

He walked away from the house without once looking back.

Through the streets streamed wailing throngs of young and

1 Dulag, or Durchgangs-lager: point outside the ghetto, where Jews were taken to be picked up by the transports.
2 Mezuzah: tiny scroll of certain excerpts from the Bible, set in containers on the doorposts of most Jewish homes.

57

old. At that time it seemed that being driven out of your home was the greatest calamity. Vevke walked straight ahead, tight-lipped, his greasy overalls shiny with use, the cobblers' table high on his shoulder, spreading cheer and courage to his right and to his left: "Jews, no tears! The butchers are giving themselves a show, a pox and a plague take them! For pity's sake, Jews, don't be giving them any treats!"

And the fact that he, Bergson, now sits in the shoe shop is also thanks to Vevke. Others would have given a mint to get themselves in here.

Vevke tosses one completed shoe after another into the basket. He works full steam. As if he meant to finish off the whole stock single-handed so the Germans shouldn't liquidate the shoe shop. In the old days this place was a hell-hole. Schultze hobbled among the tables all day. Everyone worked at a sizzling pace. The rooms were jammed beyond capacity. Then, no one dared stop for even a moment's breath. Oh, but to have those days back again. Then, you knew that here, at least, you were safe from being transported. Now even the "screwturners" don't show up any more. It's a bad omen. And Schultze's staying away from the workrooms certainly bodes no good. Now there's plenty of room at the cutting-tables, and the white patches of light between one worker's shoulder and his neighbour's cast a pall of fear. What will tomorrow bring? How will this "festiveness" end up? Meanwhile the pilgrimage to the attic proceeds as usual. Penniless cobblers gorge themselves on delicacies such as they could never dream of before the war. People sell the last stitch off their bodies. They splurge down to their last penny. No one worries about later, for no one knows whether he will have a later. No one thinks of tomorrow's bread, for no one knows whether he'll be around to buy bread tomorrow; whether he won't be dragged out of bed during the night. If so, why scrimp? To whom are they going to will it? Better hurry up to the attic, then, and buy cheese-cake, beer, roast goose, and—cyanide.

CYANIDE—

The dearest item in the canteen is cyanide. Whoever has cyanide in his pocket knows he can go ahead and eat cheese-cake.

Almost everyone in the ghetto is a solitary leftover now—without children, parents, without family. Everyone left in the ghetto has suddenly come into a fortune, become a man

58

of property. Everyone is inheriting clothing, linen, house-wares of deported relatives. Hardly have you managed to eat up the inheritance of one relative when you learn you've come into the property of another relative. What a bounty of relatives! Before, you couldn't get a thing out of them. Not only that, they never stopped complaining about why you're not helping them. One and all a lot of paupers. Now you go dragging the leftover baggage from their hovels and groan under the load a twofold groan: half for the heavy load, half for the deported relative.

And you drag some more.

There's nothing the Christians won't buy from the Jews nowadays: linen, bedding, kitchenware. Everything. The residents of the nearby Aryan streets suddenly went on a buying spree: "Bargains" of deported Jews! They heard that after liquidating the Jews in the ghettos, the Germans grab everything for themselves. Even a used baby carriage is a high-premium item. They don't leave a thing behind. Send everything to their families in Germany. So, the Poles hurry to beat the Germans to it. "Bargains!" All—from the intelligentsia to the masses—greedily await the ghetto traders. Their eyes are hungrily glued to the locked ghetto gates. They are ready to pay anything for the "bargains." Even more than they are worth. A craze has seized the Aryan streets: "Bargains"! A contagious disease. An epidemic that doesn't by-pass a single house. At the last moment of their lives, destitute cobblers have suddenly become tycoons. Like a person in a dying coma suddenly, at the final moment, open-ing clear, conscious eyes, as though he has just brought back from somewhere a brand-new life.

But the cobblers know what is going to happen to them in the moment to come. So they make for the cheese-cake in the attic.

In the shoe shop, the people suddenly become aware of the material they are using for making the shoes. More than once does the furious clatter of a sewing machine dribble off as if joining its operator in thought. While sewing, the operator notices that the "mate" now sliding from under the machine needle is cut from striped trousers such as he is now wearing on his own body. And at the cutting-table, someone will suddenly stop, his knife point not quite touch-ing the neatly arranged cloth stack. A shudder suddenly runs through him when he places his other hand on the stack and feels the material under his open palm. As though he were now resting his hand on a human shoulder with the knife poised in his other hand. The blade is suspended just over the material. In a second he will plunge the knife in full force. The blade will sink deep, deep. Pierce another jacket. Another jacket. And cut . . . cut . . .

He can't—

Passing the doorway of the rag room, the pile of old clothes insinuates itself into the corner of his eye. All at once, it seems as though people like himself are lying there, like everyone else working here. His footsteps waver, halt. The people seem to be calling him to lie down together with them on the pile. That's where he belongs, anyway.

His feet give. He can't move another step. His throat feels chokingly dry. Where had he meant to go? There's nothing he wants any more. There is no more strength for wanting. Suddenly his hand starts trembling. He wants to reach out, hold on to something, save himself. His choking breath now quivers in the palm of his hand. If there were now in the palm of his hand the bit of white cyanide he would be able to go on breathing. Only the quivering bit of cyanide can free him from the fear cutting off his breath. Cyanide! Only that can give him the strength to go on living. All at once his feet tear away from the spot—

Another cobbler has made for the attic.

"See how those shoe-fakers of mine have flown the coop!" Vevke booms at the empty benches. "All we need now is for Schultze to pop in!"

He rears up from his seat and heads for the attic.

When Vevke got there, he suddenly halted, hand on the banister, foot poised on the stair next to the last. He could not move another step. The former pain, the grief for his two missing sons, came back in all its intensity when he saw Daniella standing at the attic entrance waiting for the door to open. He forgot why he had come. He went up to her, as if this had been the reason for his coming, took her by the arm and silently walked her down the stairs.

She let him lead her. Neither resisting nor acquiescing. She moved mechanically, as in a daze. Vevke found no word to still the pain devouring his heart. He did not scold her or try to console her. He kept silent.

His guiding hand exuded plain goodness, simple love of

60

fellow man. As when a person lifts a bird out of a trap, caresses it, wants to heal it, but doesn't know how.

On returning to the shoe shop, Vevke suddenly remembered why he had left in the first place and rushed right back to the attic.

6

DANIELLA was ripping the seams of a summer coat. The colour of the silken material was light. The twilight sun glared blindingly through the rag-room window, and the seam-rippers' knives seemed to be smeared with blood. Harry sat beside her. She was teaching him seam-ripping.

"See, Harry? Watch. You put a foot on one end of the garment—like this—and the other end you hold fast under your left arm. With the fingers of the left hand you stretch the garment tight like . . ." She was about to say "like a violin" but she immediately swallowed the word. She didn't want to remind him of his beloved violin which he used to hold this way. She quickly said ". . . like something tight. And the knife in your right hand you draw lightly back and forth over the taut seam. Get it, Harry?"

"It's not so hard to understand," he said.

She moved closer to him. It was good to feel him so near.

"I always wished we could work together," she said. "Sitting by the rag heap I always used to wish you were sitting beside me. Why should you be in one shop and I in another? Why couldn't we work together? Hundreds of people work here. Why shouldn't you be one of them? Tell me, Harrik, isn't it wonderful to be sitting together?"

Harry's head was bowed over the garment he was ripping. He appeared to be completely engrossed in his work. He didn't answer.

"Doesn't it feel good?" she repeated.

He didn't look up from his work. "Lower your voice," he said. "They can hear every word. Is talking allowed here?"

"Why not? Here there's freedom. Complete freedom. Here Vevke is boss." She said it as if this were a factory belonging to her father.

The knives were smeared with the blood of the red sunset.

61

As though it were live arteries they were cutting. The sun streamed in like a gigantic red floodlight. Daniella wondered at her being able to look straight through the light beam at the sun without being blinded. As a rule, she had only to lift her eyes just a little to the sun and they would immediately smart with pain. Now the sun was wan, cold, as if cut out of tinsel. This is the first time in her life she has ever looked right at the sun. She felt as though she were seeing into the sky; as if she had conquered the fiery sun.

"Harry, see the sun? Now you can see what it really looks like, in all its nakedness."

"That's no sun, that's a hoax," he said. He didn't raise his eyes. As if it were not worth his looking.

"To you everything is a hoax. You don't believe in anything any more."

He didn't answer. She was amazed how quickly he was ripping.

"Harry," she said, "from now on I won't believe either. I won't believe a thing any more. They said you were deported in a transport. So how can you be sitting here with me? From now on I'm not believing anything either."

Harry didn't look up from his work. He said:

"You can't be 'deported' any more. It's the same everywhere."

She didn't understand what he was saying. But lately she'd been used to hearing him say things she didn't understand. She didn't ask him to explain now, either. She thought: Maybe he really was deported, but on the way he jumped the train. Stecklman, of Heller's second court, also jumped the transport train and made it back to the ghetto with four bullets in his body. Maybe Harry was also shot while escaping, but isn't letting on. He never tells anything. Such things are really better untold. He should only not let it slip to anyone! He's become so devil-may-care lately. When she first learned he'd been deported, she tried to console herself with the thought that he might jump the train, like Stecklman. She had a feeling he would. It was her only hope. It was what enabled her to go on living.

"I was going to buy cyanide," she said. "They sell it at our canteen. Don't you ever go up there! Promise, Harrik?"

"Go up there? What for! It's just some more fraud. They're only out to bilk you. Everything is fraud. Even the death they carry."

"What do you mean? I don't understand a word you're saying."

"Why don't you understand?" he snapped. "These days a man has no way of knowing if he's already in the hereafter, or if he still has to wait for death. Everything is mixed up. Life and death in one brew. A hereafter that's not here, not after. Fraud and hoax. What's so hard to understand?"

He spoke rapidly and harshly. There was something queer about it. She knew she had written these same words in her diary; but hearing them now from Harry she somehow couldn't seem to make sense out of them. Suddenly she suspected Harry had read what she had written in the diary and was now mocking her words. The words irk him, that's why he's so mad at her.

She was too embarrassed to accuse him of having looked into her diary without permission. It dawned on her that only Fella could have shown him the diary. Fella's bed is near the window, and Fella sees her tucking the notebook into the slot between the sill and the cooling box. Another one of Fella's pranks. She didn't want to be mad at Harry now. It would be a shame to spoil the wonderful feeling of sitting beside him. Just remembering the moment she was told he'd been deported was enough to put her in the seventh heaven at their being together.

The light seam thread of the silken raincoat snapped like little nuts under the knife blade. The split thread on both sides of the seam looked like two rows of tiny bared teeth.

Harry turned his head to her.

"Let me show you a neater trick," he said, and with both hands began pulling at a paper-wrapped package in his trouser pocket. The package came out with difficulty. She looked at the protruding end of the package and was sure it was bread he had brought for her. She was about to tell him she would under no circumstances eat the bread, he'd better remember that—when he finally got it out, unwrapped it, and lifted out the dilapidated man's shoe of the Oswiencim girl. She wondered whether it was the same shoe or its mate which Harry had brought along with him escaping from Auschwitz. Harry clutched the toe of the shoe with both hands and ripped the upper off the sole. Suddenly it looked as though he were holding open the jaws of a crocodile. The two rows of white wooden pegs looked like jagged teeth in the crocodile's maw. It didn't faze her at all. She wanted to tell him so, when Schultze suddenly came hobbling rapidly toward them, aiming the tip of his cane at Harry's face. The rubber tip circled over Harry's face like a wasp with drawn stinger about to alight on its victim. When the cane tip finally settled on Harry's face, between the two eyes, Schultze screeched, "From Auschwitz the shoe came and to Auschwitz it will return! But together with you, my dear. Off to Gestapo now. But quick! ..."

She felt Harry's fingers pressing her hand. He pulled her after him and they raced down the stairs into the big shoe storeroom. They hid behind the high wooden shelves where the shoes were lined up row upon row. The shafts of setting sun blazed through the window and glared in their eyes. Daniella knew that soon their pursuers would be looking for them here. They'll be spotted, but they won't be able to see their pursuers because of the blinding sun. She had sinned against the sun before. She had imagined she had conquered it. That's why the sun is taking it out on her now. She was about to ask Harry why he had to go and pry open the Auschwitz shoe and turn it into a crocodile's maw. It only infuriated the Germans. But just then, Harry whispered into her ear, as if to justify himself: "I'll go on tearing the shoe's maw or it will swallow me alive. Do you want it to devour me as it did Ferber? I won't let it. I'm stronger than they!"

Beyond the open door black-uniformed Germans were stumping up the stairs to the workroom. Daniella knew it was for them they were coming. Her knees began quaking. Harry looked at her. She wanted to calm down but couldn't quell the trembling of her knees. As though some outside force were shaking them from within. The sun poured red sheaves of light in among the shoes arrayed on the shelves, and they looked like marching ranks of feet wading in blood. Maybe the Germans will go easier on them if they give themselves up. And as if in reply to her thought, Harry opened the window and they jumped out. They ran across the road toward the woods. Heavily armed Germans on motor cycles whizzed up and down the road. They were now on the Aryan side, where a Jew mustn't be seen. They were outside the ghetto. Harry ripped the yellow star off his jacket. Seeing Daniella vacillating, he reached out and ripped the shame-sign off her breast. The spot where the star had been stood out, unfaded. The dark points of the Star of David showed clearly. She wanted to cry for fear.

64

They ran through the thicket. The thick underbrush entangled their feet and hampered their flight. She knew the Germans were bearing down on them. The prickly shrubs stung and scratched her face. She couldn't run any more. Her feet became like attached blocks of wood which she now had to lug as she ran. "Buck up! Buck up! If you can't run now it'll be all over with you! . . ." Harry shouted as he ran. She fell behind him. She felt her strength draining.

"Run, Harry, save yourself!" she cried. She felt the Germans were near.

"Keep going! For pity's sake, don't let yourself think. If you can't run without thinking you'll be finished!" he shouted back to her.

. . . Yablova woods! How did the Yablova woods get here? She's in Metropoli! Among the trees, not far from her, German is being spoken. She clearly hears Germans speaking. Where should she run? Who will let her in? In the Polish hut where she had fled from Yablova market-place, the Pole's teeth, tongue, and open mouth barked into her eyes: "A Yid? Go on, get out! . . ." The shrubs pricked her face. She ran. Ran. With her last wind. Ran, ran. "A Yid? Go on, get out!"

Where was Harry? She no longer saw him near her. Her feet dragged like huge stones from both sides of her body. She could no longer carry their dead weight. "*Get out! . . . Get out! . . .*" The stone feet dragged her down, down. She slumped to the ground. She felt herself sinking into a deep pit. Suddenly she felt the ground beneath her. She saw her feet lying outside, on the surface of the ground. She heard the approach of the Germans but she lay rooted to the ground. She was unable to dislodge herself. The footsteps drew nearer, nearer. As though they were tramping right by her ears. She raised her head—*Schultze!* He seemed to be swooping down at her out of the sky. The black Gestapo cap on his head gives him an air of grim festiveness. He aims the black pellet at the tip of his cane directly at her eyes. The cane stretches ever longer, until it is outlandishly long. Schultze stands at the other end of the outstretched cane. His face is cruelly studious. He doesn't say a word. Just stretches the cane towards her face, searching for a good spot on which to set the rubber tip. She knows Schultze is preparing to inflict a horrible death on her. She strains with all her might but cannot move. She screams but the screams don't come out of her throat. The tip of the cane looms nearer, larger. Her eyes are in a frozen gape. She can't clamp them shut. Any moment and the tip will plunge deep into them. It will suck out the last drop of her blood. Schultze's face is cruelly studious. She reaches out to wrench the cane away. But the cane is ungraspable. Like air. . . . It's useless trying to save herself. No one will come to her rescue here. Her screams don't come out of her throat. *"If you can't run it'll be all over with you! . . ."* Suddenly she sees Harry standing bound in the white silken raincoat she had ripped in the rag room that morning. The Germans grab hold of him and force him to look and see what Schultze is about to do to her. Harry collapses. He faints. She starts screaming: "Harry! Harry! Harry!"

A full moon was framed in the window. Everything was cast with a cold, silvery light. Daniella didn't know where she was. She felt her neck clamped between her own fingers. She thought she was still lying in Yablova woods. Her screams still rang in her ears. Had she really screamed? She couldn't make out the Centre. She didn't recognize the room in which she lay. A pale shaft of light reached from the moon directly into her eyes—cold, rigid, vampiric. Like Schultze's outstretched cane. Her hands were clammy. Her body was drenched in cold sweat. She was afraid to move. But when she sidled her eyes about the room, she saw the Oswiencim girl returning to her bed with the black man's shoe hugged to her heart.

Daniella wanted to call out to the girl and ask her if she had heard her cries for help. But her mouth wouldn't open.

From the beds around her rose a loud snoring. The flowers of Hayim-Idl's Spanish wall were bathed in the frigid light of the moon. The dream now unwound before her eyes like a segment of life embalmed in the dark celluloid of a film reel. The film unwinds, and the embalmed life is condemned once more to live a life borrowed as the frigid light of the moon. The dream springs at you to possess you anew and within you again live a borrowed life.

The moonbeam crept slowly up the tile stove. The white tiles returned the moon a lurid stare.

Everything now seemed inescapable, past all hope. Mute tears ran from her eyes. She felt like a pariah, hounded day and night. Crushed, forlorn, with no one to help her. The

66

realities of day are no better than the nightmares at night.

She heard the patter of footsteps on the cobblestones in the yard. She didn't know what time it was. It was the night towards Sunday—a bleak, prospectless Sunday, a night of utter despair. A lunar night white and terrifying as cyanide; pale and hollow as the vampiric light of the moon. She sat up and started dressing. Everything happening in the ghetto could no longer be stopped or undone. Only the "dot" due to emerge Sunday from behind the big mountain gnawed relentlessly at the heart and glimmered illusively in her mind, like the illusory light of the moon. The thought that she would soon be standing in the soup-compound watching the "dot" approach coiled about her heart like a viper, and coursed into her bloodstream like its white venom.

She tried to untangle the knotty laces of her high sport-boots. Reesha Meyerchik had exactly the same shoes. They had ordered them together at the same store. When they were fleeing from Yablova market she had no idea Reesha was shot. Reesha kept pace with her as they ran, sometimes even getting ahead of her. It was only when they got to the woods that she noticed Reesha's blood trailing on the ground. There wasn't a single hut into which she was permitted to bring the shot girl. Just one old man took pity on her and pointed to Izzy the tinsmith's closed workshop: "Better yell for him in Yiddish," he said. "Knock for him to open. Maybe the Germans haven't killed him yet."

Off in a hidden corner of the workshop, the tinsmith and his wife lay on the floor behind a pile of scrap iron and rusty tin sheets. His face also looked like a rusty scrap of tin. He turned to his wife and said, "A Jewish girl is bleeding to death in Yablova woods . . ." The woman gazed up at her husband's head from the floor. Her eyes cried mute protest over the futility of her life and her husband's life which he now intends to throw over. She did not answer. "I'm going," the tinsmith said. She gazed up at his head and said nothing.

Daniella heard footsteps hurrying over the cobblestones down in the yard. Stecklman jumped the train. Maybe Harry did, too. Maybe when she goes out to the soup-compound as usual she'll suddenly see him coming to her. The image of Harry swathed in white floated up before her eyes. What is this thing which keeps coming up in her dreams? What does it signify? From now on she'll draw the curtain over the window on moonlight nights. Dreams! Oh, you cold, vampiric night mirrors, set over against our lived days like the moonshine opposite the sun; mirrors which suck the pith from the seeds implanted in our fate and reflect it back at us on a night of moon shrewish as an old hag—a gossip-monger; so by night the dreams sough into our ears the weaving rumours of our destiny. "It's all a dream," Harry had said. Was his deportation to a labour camp also just a dream? Will she really suddenly hear Daddy's whistle waking her for school? Or is it just that the blinds of her room are not drawn now, and that's why the moon is enmeshing her this way in its silvery web?

She went down to the gate.

II

Night withdrew across the sky like a foe from conquered land, leaving ruin, mourning, and casualties in its wake.

One by one the pallid shadows emerged from the three courts towards the gate. She saw and didn't see them coming; this time she was one of them. Like them, she came down here because of the calamity which had driven her from bed. The same calamity. The same grief. They will run out frenziedly: maybe they can still help. And she will run out like them: maybe Harry will come from the fields. She is now standing among them, one of many and exactly like them. She looks at them and doesn't see them, just as they look at her and don't see her. She knows it's crazy: Harry isn't coming! She'll never see him again! But she doesn't want to believe it. The others also know their running is useless. They'll never see their loved ones again. It's always that way: dragged from the house in the dead of night, and never seen again. It's always that way, but nobody wants to believe it.

The militiamen haven't looked in lately to see if the illegals are all sleeping at the Centre. The militiamen are busy at nights hauling people from their beds. Queer that they should still let the illegals stay at the Centre. "Illegals!" The word sounds like some diabolic joke. Who isn't illegal nowadays? The whole ghetto is like a burning ship far at sea. Harry—the "legal," the "secure" one—has gone to his doom; she—the "illegal"—is still around. When a fire breaks out in prison, the secure ones, those waiting to go free, perish; those condemned to death save themselves. Today they are deporting workers from "non-war-essential" factories. Till just a short while back these workers felt so snug and secure, and now—they are in the death camps. But she, the "illegal," is still permitted to sleep in her bed, because she has a labour card from the Labour Commissioner's shoe shop. Death is a blind reaper. Never misses. It's all the same to him who falls first and who falls later. But the heads that are left outside his swath a while—they imagine death has deliberately by-passed them. Just as Zalke put it: "The ghetto is like a sack full of seeds. The German reaches into the sack now and then and grabs himself a fistful. Any seeds that slip between his fingers get a bit of a reprieve . . ." They say all is quiet in Kongressia ghetto now. The ghetto is sealed tight as a nailed-up crate. Everybody works in one big shop. Daddy and Mommy are probably living with a lot of other families in one room. Their bed must be off in a corner, like Fella's bed here. And Moni—with a yellow star against his heart. Maybe Daddy has also fixed himself some sort of "villa" like Hayim-Idl's, and they live there in a private corner of their own. Daddy always liked to have his shaving kit ready in the bathroom on the blue marble shelf under the mirror. Where does he keep it now? If he has a window, he probably puts it on the sill. There is no window in Hayim-Idl's "villa." Wonder why Hayim-Idl didn't put up his "villa" in the corner by the store. Then his "villa" would also have a window.

The cobblestones in the first court glisten as though freshly scrubbed. Must have rained during the night. How was it she hadn't noticed day breaking? She had been sitting there wide awake looking at the window all the time. Right here the man with the JUDE branded on his brow had lain. The Judenrat deported Shlamek together with his mother, because both were living off the soup-kitchen. Good thing Shlamek went with his mother. He'll be able to take care of her, there. The woman had been very sick toward the end. If she herself had been deported with Harry, she'd have gone gladly. Harry had looked very bad lately. If she knew where he was, she'd volunteer to go there on the next transport. Mrs. Heller is already on guard over the remainder of her bookcase. All day long she's at the window, watching the remnants of the case by the fence. The doors were stolen off long ago, but from within, the memory of her two sons still glimmers at her.

In a corner of the third court is Vevke's ramshackle hovel. From here the hovel resembles a hen roosting up on a ladder in the dark. The janitor had put it together before the war from some broken planks, for a tool shed. The place wasn't meant for more than that.

How did she get here? She didn't even feel her feet taking her. Why has she come here? The rising morning contemplated the miserable planks of the hovel and the sagging roof, the way, in the ghetto after an Aktion, they contemplate an abandoned child whom the Germans have forgotten to include on the transport with her parents. She felt so tired. She was standing near a pile of refuse and scrap that had been cleared out of the houses to make room for the people. She sat down on the edge of a broken stove—useless, discarded. Suddenly, she also felt like a piece of useless, unwanted scrap thrown out. Everything around her, useless: the new day coming up, the sky, the earth—all meaningless, futile.

A yearning seized her. An incoherent yearning. She didn't know for what, whom. She was terribly lonely. She wanted the door of the hovel to open, someone to come out of there, take her inside. She so wanted someone's breast to cry on, to feel the nearness of a human being. A human being. To see a warm look in human eyes. Why is she going to the fields now? Harry won't be coming. The pain of his not coming frightened her. She wanted for someone devoted and understanding not to let her go to the fields, to hold her back. It was all so hopeless. She wanted for someone to console her, and she wanted to have the feeling of refusing to be consoled.

That time, when Tedek was deported, she didn't feel this way. She first sees it now. But Vevke must have felt then the way she feels now. And she never had the thoughtfulness even once to come to Vevke and share his grief. Tedek's family probably hasn't forgiven her for this. She knows they blame her for Tedek's going out of the ghetto. How can she expect them to feel sorry for her now? Why didn't she ever come here before at dawn to sit on this rubbish heap? Why only now that Harry has been deported?

In a rotting baby's shoe lying on the ground by her feet, a tall green blade of grass pushed through a rent in the sole.

The rising sun gilded the dewdrops on the leaf and they glittered like jewels.

Hurrying footsteps sounded from the street. She started up. She went to the gate. Already there was no one there.

III

The soup-kitchen compound was deserted. The little soup-window was boarded up. There was no sign that soup had ever been distributed here. Not a trace was left of the people who had once partaken of the soup here. But the house was still called "Judenrat Free Soup Kitchen."

Lonely and forlorn she stood at the edge of the compound. Every corner here reminded her of Harry. The air was full of the memory of him. But there was no more Harry. She had no idea what a German labour camp was; that no one knew. But everyone did know what the Germans were. Maybe at this very moment Harry is standing somewhere working till he collapses. She could not endure the thought, but there was no escaping it.

The fields were empty; the mountain, mute and desolate. A gnawing yearning rippled across the fields from the mountain to her heart, from her heart to the mountain. She knew Harry would not be coming any more. But her eyes did not give up watching: any moment now, any instant, and a little dot will appear there . . . . Thousand times a moment she felt the tingling of Harry's coming, and thousand times a moment the disappointment of his not coming twinged her heart.

She couldn't bear to stand in the empty compound any more. An irresistible force drew her to the opposite side of the mountain, from where Harry used to come and from where he would never come again. She could no longer contain the storm within her.

She started to run.

IV

She did not see the mountain. The closer she got to it the more it melted before her eyes. Jew-Quarter 3 gradually disappeared behind her. At close range everything here looked different. The sun poured its yellow light into the

71

jaundiced crevices of the jagged mountain slope. Many footpaths wound here. Every granule of sand breathed the intimacy of Harry's footsteps. She felt the footsteps. She could touch them with her hands.

Across the fields the first hovels of Jew-Quarter 1 began to appear. On the left stretched the railway lines. They gleamed in the sun like silvery stripes on dark cloth in the rag room. Far, far off a lone locomotive, big as a toy, smoked near two trees.

She was running.

All this time, she had managed only twice to get to Harry's home. When Abram the trader had good customers and it paid him to bribe the militia secretary for a one-trip transit pass for Daniella, so she could smuggle his goods across to Jew-Quarter 1 under her wide raincoat. Daniella jumped at the chance, not for the money, but for the few minutes she would be able to spend at Harry's.

As Daniella now opened the door to Harry's room, everything suddenly seemed strange, unrecognizable, as if she had stumbled into a wrong address. She saw Ferber's eyes raised toward her from where he was sitting. He came toward her slowly, and without a word took her by the arm, led her to the chair, the way you lead a person who seems about to faint. He sat her down. Her arrival here now seemed self-explanatory.

A mournful stillness hung in the room. Sanya was sitting on a wooden cot, facing Harry's empty bed. There was no spread on the bed. It was made up, as though awaiting his return from the night shift. A white emptiness showed from beyond the back-folded corner of the blanket. Sanya sat facing the empty whiteness and did not take her eyes off it.

The room was bare. The furniture was all gone. The cupboard, the beds—everything had been sold for bread. Stark, stripped walls. Just a rickety little table in the corner and an old iron stove with a broken-off pipe. On a long nail protruding from the door-post hung Harry's coat, the coat in which he used to come to her. Over the coat hung his hat. He had apparently gone to work without hat and coat, and hatless and coatless was taken away.

She wanted to run up to the coat and hug it. A sleeve hung from the shoulder—full, round, alive. The end of the sleeve was limp, empty. But it still seemed to her she could see

Harry's white hand there. She wanted to run over and grasp the sleeve like a live hand. Harry . . . Harry . . . But Sanya's rigid shoulders, her stony gaze rooted to the empty bed, froze her to the spot.

It was almost a week that Harry had been gone, and the room still seemed as though a dead body were lying on the ground, the soul flitting into all the corners, resting on every object. The melancholy, brooding stillness lingered in the room as though the pains were here to stay for all eternity. Sanya was dressed in her blue overalls, her hair tidily combed back, but her face was like a waxen mask.

. . . She could never have pictured Sanya looking like this. God knows what she's decided to do to herself. That moment she forgot that she herself had stood at the door of the shoe-shop attic. The lifeless expression on Sanya's face made her forget about herself. Now in Harry's room, it suddenly struck her for the first time: maybe the deportees aren't killed after all . . . What will happen when Harry comes home and hears what happened to Sanya? Vevke, too, keeps insisting that Tedek will come back. Who'll take care of Sanya now?

Ferber sat immersed in thought, his eyes fixed on the ground, not saying a word. Maybe he and Sanya had been discussing something before she came, but her sudden appearance revived the memory of Harry and stirred up the pain in all its intensity. Now Ferber was silent, like one who can find no word of condolence for the bereaved whose deceased still lies before him.

The ache of smothered tears now wept from the depleted walls. Heavy sorrow draped Sanya's shoulders. How long is it since the whole family sat around the table in Kongressia? The whole house used to ring with Sanya's gay laughter. In the next Aktion they're liable to deport her, the way it happens to all wives of deported men. Who'll look after Sanya now? Who will take care of her?

Sanya got up. She went over to the window. The blinds were drawn all the way. All the houseware now lay there. She unrolled a white napkin. Inside were wrapped half a loaf and a knife. She spread the napkin on the table before Daniella, and said:

"Eat, Dani—"

Daniella raised her eyes to her. "*Eat, Dani* . . ." She could no longer hold back. Just the way Harry had spoken to her. She threw her arms around Sanya's waist and burst into bitter crying.

Sanya stood motionless. She just pressed Daniella's head to her belly. The weeping intensified. It seemed to be coming out of Sanya's belly. It was a mutual weeping over one and the same person whom both, each in her own way, loved more than all else in the world.

Sanya stood motionless.

"Harry will come back, Sanya. The war will end . . ."

Sanya raised Daniella's head to her with both hands. They were in clinging embrace—Daniella sitting, Sanya standing. Out of Daniella's eyes Harry's blue glance looked up at her. Not just the eyes; all of Daniella's face now evoked Harry: the same chiselled mouth, the same twin white rows of teeth, the identical shadow between the lower lip and chin.

"Harry will soon be coming home," Sanya said softly.

"You mean it, Sanya?" Daniella started up. "You really mean it?"

"I've a promise. I'm waiting."

"Is there really a chance that Harry will be coming back before the end of the war? You're not saying it just to make me feel better? Who promised?"

Sanya tried to evade the question. She went on looking into Daniella's blue eyes. Her lips whispered, "Everything is possible, my baby. Everything is possible. If Harry doesn't come to me, I'll come to him."

The sudden quiver of Daniella's body between her hands jolted Sanya as out of a trance. The words she had just uttered suddenly reached her ears. She wished she could unsay them. Ferber also looked up from the floor. Sanya tore herself away, smoothed the wrinkled napkin on the table and picked up a glass to bring Daniella some tea.

"Which way did you come, Daniella?" she asked.

"Same way as Harry used to come to me every Sunday."

"Harry never went without a transit pass—forged, but still a slip of paper to show! Why do you take such risks? Aren't things bad enough?" Deep anguish furrowed Sanya's face.

Ferber interjected, "The risks aren't always exactly where people think they are. Harry wasn't caught crossing from one Jew-Quarter to the other."

Sanya was walking toward the door with the glass in her hand. She meant to go to a neighbour to get Daniella the tea. But hearing Ferber's caustic remark, she stopped short,

74

facing the door. She said, "You don't meant to suggest, do you, that Daniella should be roaming among the Jew-Quarters without a piece of paper?"

"I mean to suggest," Ferber raised his head to Sanya's back, "that Daniella should join the Kibbutz.[1] A big Aktion is brewing in the ghetto, and if I'm not mistaken it's going to be a girls' Aktion."

"Ferber!" Sanya wheeled around. "Daniella works in the Labour Commissioner's shoe shop. What could be safer?"

Sanya went out to the corridor. Ferber lowered his head again, went back to staring at the floor, said no more.

Daniella suddenly felt like someone eavesdropping on a conversation about herself. The exchange between Ferber and Sanya, particularly the tone in which the words were spoken, seemed to her like a continuation, almost a playback of a stormy debate which had been raging before she got here and had been momentarily interrupted only because of her arrival.

Daniella didn't know too much about the "Kibbutz." What she did know was that this was a hush-hush word in the ghetto. She also knew that Tedek had belonged to the "Kibbutz," and that after his brother Menashe was killed in the Slavic Woods, Tedek never again so much as mentioned the word. And she knew that many who have no labour cards are members of the "Kibbutz" and that these boys and girls had let the Judenrat know that they would resist with arms any attempt to transport them: "We'll get in our shots at the Germans and the whole ghetto will go up in flames, Judenrat and all!" And as the grapevine has it, Monyek Matroz, head of the Judenrat, is afraid of this warning and reckons with it.

Sanya returned to the room with a glass of steaming tea in her hand. She urged Daniella to eat and hurry back to her quarter, because noon-time is best for sneaking over from one Jew-Quarter to the other.

When Daniella stood by the door ready to leave, Ferber pulled a forged transit pass out of his pocket—something to show, just in case—and without a word handed it to her.

[1] Kibbutz: Hebrew term for communal settlement.

7

AT the Centre everybody was already asleep. After a back-breaking work-day one collapses into bed in the evening the way, in the Gestapo torture cellar, one falls into the releasing arms of swoon. Sleep is but a brief respite during an unceasing siege of pain. Hardly does one manage to get one's eyes shut than night is over and one has to dash off to the shop again.

Suddenly— A battering at the house gate ...

In the ghetto, when there is a knocking at the gate at night, it reverberates in the heart as though a thousand alarm bells were heaving inside you. For it is death now knocking at the gate. And who knows whose soul he has come for this time?

Fella is composed as ever. She placidly opens her eyes, looks around. On the beds right and left sit upsprung naked shoulders, terrified heads. Fella shuts her eyes again and snuggles up in the blanket as if all this were none of her concern. She has a good Special Card from the chief of the Judenrat Militia. She can go right back to sleep. It's not the likes of her they're after.

Hanna and Tzivia, the two Chebin sisters, sit trembling on their beds. The danger has struck at them out of their sleep and is coiling itself about their drowsy, half-naked bodies with a well-known yet unfamiliar terror. True, they also have labour cards, but not from a "war-essential" factory. Isn't it for them that they're now pounding at the gate?

Hayim-Idl in his white union suit scurries from window to window, peeps out now around the corner of this window, now around the corner of the other window. He doesn't know, and can't make up his mind, whether to wake the baby first or to stow her away in some place while she's still asleep. Meanwhile, the seconds flash by and the minutes sharpen like knives before the eyes. Running feet on the yard cobblestones blare into his ears: *"Someone has already gone to open the gate!"* The news spreads throughout his whole being. The hair roots prick the skull like hot needles. The skin tightens and stiffens. Death is breathing down on it.

It's not about himself and his wife that Hayim-Idl is

76

terrified. They both work in the shoe shop. But the heart convulses: what if this is a children's Aktion?

At the mere thought that they're liable to take the baby away from him, the whites of his eyes bulge from their sockets. He shuttles back and forth between the walls and doesn't know where to run, what to do. Every minute counts. The head is about to burst. Fear rapidly tosses idea after idea, plan after plan into the mind, piles them up like a growing scrap heap. Where to run? What to do next? What to do now? So he scurries from window to window, from corner to corner, and doesn't do a thing.

His wife Dvortche, who has lately stopped hearing altogether, even when being shouted into the ear, seems, however, to have heard the knocking at the gate. For the knocking at the gate in the dead of night is heard not in the ears, but in the heart, with the bottom drop of blood in the veins. So she began pulling out all the forbidden goods concealed in the chest table—the sheets of felt, the hatbands, the hats—and hurled them all pellmell to the floor. Let the Germans take it all from her now! Let them punish her for it! She scoops up the sleeping infant, hugs her to her heart: Only don't let her wake up . . . not let out a sound! She bends over the open chest, lays sweet little Bella carefully on the left-over felt pieces. She stands bent over the chest, as though she were gingerly laying her own heart there. Very slowly she closes the chest, spreads a tablecloth over it so it should again look like a table. She doesn't talk; just sways. Lips sealed, clenched—and sways . . .

Hayim-Idl looks on at his wife's actions and doesn't know how he can help her. His knees quake. With a convulsive foot he shoves the thrown-out felts lying on the floor into a corner, as though he didn't trust his own body to bend without keeling over. His lower jaw twitches, spits out words as if he had just chewed them: ". . . last . . . goods . . . let it . . . let it . . . ransom . . . take it, God . . . not my baby. . ."

Daniella is sitting on her bed. Her head is full and empty. She looks about with petrified eyes: the bed of the Oswiencim girl is empty! . . . Just before night curfew she slipped out of the Centre. No one even noticed that she hadn't come back. The emptiness of her bed intensifies the fear. The lit candle in Hayim-Idl's "villa" gleams in the window with black, uncanny night. Each blow at the gate comes running up to the foot of every bed like a herald come to announce

77

the imminent arrival of a gruesome master. Daniella clenches
her teeth to stop them from chattering. But she has no reason
to be afraid! She has a labour card from the Labour Commissioner's own shoe shop! And Vevke won't leave her in
the lurch! Still, fear is contagious, and chattering teeth won't
be calmed by logic when there is pounding at the ghetto gate
in the dead of night.

On the bed opposite Daniella the two Chebin sisters sit
huddled up against each other, like two hens out in a snow-
storm, silent and shivering.

Boots. Terrifying German boots stumping up the stairs.
As though their hobnails were treading on the naked flesh.
The door is being stormed. Hayim-Idl's look rolls out of his
gaping eye-sockets, brushes over the narrow beds, and stops
dead on the empty bed of the Oswiencim girl. The door
strains inward. Everyone is numb, paralysed with fear. Never
have the two door halves arched in this way, as if trying
desperately to recoil from the German voices raging at them.
Another moment and the door halves will burst open. Hayim-
Idl's feet tear themselves free. He runs to open the door.

Gestapo! Just behind them—blue-white caps of Judenrat
Militia.

The Gestapoman is holding a list in his hands. Odd, death
has ordinary hands, white, human hands—

The Gestapoman reads names from the list: Fella, the
Chebin sisters, the Oswiencim girl, Daniella . . .

"On the double! Dress! Snap to it! . . ."

Fella whips the Special Card out of her coat and hands it
to the militiaman: Must be some mistake—how did her name
get on such a list?

"Here's my Special Card, signed and sealed by the militia
chief," she states coolly, confidently.

The Gestapoman snatches the card, rips it to shreds and
throws them in Fella's face.

"Snap to it! Move! Quicker!"

. . . No! She won't show her labour card now, Daniella
quickly decides. The Gestapoman is liable to tear it up
without even looking at it. How will she prove afterwards
that she really works in the shoe shop? No, she mustn't let
go of her labour card. Her whole life now depends on this
yellow piece of paper with the red swastika stamp. She'll
show it at militia headquarters. Better go along with the
others now. But the knees tremble so. But why do the knees

tremble so? The Gestapoman is watching. Better hurry up and dress. The fingers don't hold on to the clothes. Maybe Vevke will come tomorrow morning to get her out of the militia. After all, she has to show up for work—

"Move! Move! On the double!"

The Gestapoman gave Hanna a prodding kick with his foot. Hanna wanted to take along her prayer book. Her sister Tzivia can't contain herself any more. The Gestapoman's roar contracts her bowels. The congested fear in her stomach bursts out in a stream of faeces.

"Filthy shitbags!"

Now of all times Daniella just can't seem to get her other foot into the shoe. The laces of the high sport boot are all knotted up. When she went to bed last night, she pushed it off with her foot without unlacing it. She was tired. The pistol gleams black in the Gestapoman's white hand. If her finger-tips don't stop trembling, she'll have to go with one bare foot. After all, she works in the shoe shop. Why is she so frightened? Calm—Calm—She mustn't lose her head and forget to take along things she might need on the way. Actually she doesn't have anything. On top of the high tiled stove are three filled notebooks of her diary, and in the slot between the cooling box and the wall is the last notebook. That's all she has. If Hayim-Idl could only run down now and tell Vevke they're come to take her to the labour camp, maybe Vevke could do something. After all, Vevke is the shoe-shop boss—

"Move! Quick! Scum!"

And the "scum"—four Jewish girls—crowded to push out the open door.

Hayim-Idl stands flattened against the wall. His white underwear blends with the paleness of the wall. His face is yellow. His head looks like a waxwork head someone had hung on the wall. The head stares goggle-eyed at the black back of the Gestapoman plugging the whole doorway. Death has skipped him. Seems he's still alive.

As she went out, Daniella threw towards Hayim-Idl's petrified head, "Tell Vevke . . ."

Dvortche arched back over the chest, as though wishing to block her baby's hiding place from view. She is ready for anything now. Anything. Over her dead body will they take the child from her. Within her crouched a roused mother beast, but from without she looked like a length of white felt someone had hastily flung on to the chest, its end trailing down to the floor.

Outside, a black ghetto night received them, took them into cold arms and led them off.

Where?

An odd fear mingled with curiosity seized Daniella—the eternal curiosity to find out what it's like on the other side of one's life and one's fear while being led there.

The tremor of a queer travel fever now throbbed deep in her subconscious. An echo of something was playing back in her heart . . . something familiar . . . something she had felt before . . . the time she was getting ready for the first excursion in her life.

Where is that school excursion now taking her?

II

Outside, night blotted out the dark ghetto hovels. Huge searchlights were posted on the main street for the occasion of tonight's Aktion. Their beams stabbed into the ghetto like blazing spears, spotlighting the fear. From side streets emerged black shadows of Gestapomen with machine guns, leading cowering, trembling girls just dragged out of their beds. The girls had not hidden. They had felt immune. Why, they all have genuine labour cards exempting them from labour camp.

The shoulders of the two Chebin sisters are oddly slouched. They walk ahead, with short, rapid steps, as though wanting to prove their obedience: They've been ordered to go—and look, they're going. Fella and Daniella quicken their steps, so as not to lag. The Gestapoman, pistol in hand, sullenly walks behind them. From all sides Germans and militiamen bark: "Step it up! On the double!" He doesn't get a chance to yell at them.

Monyek Matroz, head of the Judenrat, comes dashing out of a dark alley, accompanied by a cortège of senior Judenrat officials and militia officers. He dashes out of the darkness, looking very preoccupied, vanishes once more in the darkness, and emerges again. It looks as though he were consorting with the night and were whispering to her in the dark. A long white sheet flashes in his hands: not a girl is going to get out of his list tonight. None other than he, the head man of the Judenrat, is running this Aktion. The main street gradually fills with batches of girls. Here and there a gate opens and the dark ghetto hovel discharges a fresh victim, escorted by Gestapo and militia.

Ferber had said, "A major Aktion is brewing. If I'm not mistaken it'll be a girls' Aktion this time."

Now it's clear: this is a girls' night-Aktion.

"But Daniella works at the Labour Commissioner's shoe shop!" Sanya had answered. "What can be safer than that?"

How are you to know in the ghetto which is the right way?

. . . She has already been led through these same dark streets. That was the night she got here, when Vevke saved her from the transport. Now she's again being led at night through these same streets. But this time—away. Where? Where? What sort of place are all these people being led to? What do they do to them? *Why, this is a transport!* She's being taken away to a transport now! Will Vevke be able to save her this time, too? Fella, always so cocksure, is also straggling along like a lost sheep. An altogether different Fella. Not like her at all. Maybe Vevke will hurry and put in a word for her. Tell them that she was a good worker in the shop. Never missed a day, either. They can see for themselves, in the roll books. Main thing is that Hayim-Idl should hurry and tell Vevke. Judging by his face, he didn't look as if he even understood what she said.

Militiamen in blue-white caps march on either side of them. New victims are constantly being brought out of by-streets. They are marched over the pavements, middle of the street; singly and in groups. The night winds itself about them and leads them off to the mysterious unknown. The blue-white caps on the militiamen's heads phosphoresce in the distance, under the yellow searchlight beams, like the eye whites of capering demons at the head of a mute night procession.

III

The militia compound was fenced in on all sides, packed full of captured girls. Jew-Militiamen were posted at all exits.

81

Everybody was here. From the wealthiest girls to the poorest; those who had slaved in the shops, and those who had fixed themselves faked labour cards for money. The prettiest girls of the ghetto have been routed from their beds tonight and herded into the militia compound. Many of them are sure that first thing tomorrow they will be taken out of here either through pull or for a ransom. It's happened to them before. Others wring their hands desperately. Some sob loudly, with tears, and some whimper, dry-eyed. The fear of the unknown makes you shiver, as though sinister eyes were blazing at you out of the dark. Not a face, not a figure, just sinister eyes.

Fella is making a quick round of the gates, trying to get into conversation with one of the militiamen posted at the locked exits. They're all her friends from way back. Maybe they'll let her in on something. But now they are all shaking their heads. There's not a thing they can do, they reply furtively. They're not even supposed to be talking to her. Doesn't she see that the big boss himself is running the show? It's he who made up the roster for this Aktion. Every militiaman has to answer for the "heads" he'd been assigned to round up. Maybe later, at the Dulag, when the Germans clear out, if there's any surplus, why then, of course, Fella knows she'll be the first one let off. But now, not a chance in the world. Monyek is holding on to the roster.

The compound becomes fuller and fuller. They keep bringing in the girls. Who knows if the labour cards will be any good this time? Almost everybody here has one. Otherwise, they wouldn't have spent the night at home. Anyone who doesn't have a card just doesn't sleep in her bed at night. Now it all comes out: it's those who hide who are the smart ones—they don't have to work in the German shops; comes an Aktion and they're not found; and when they need girls for the labour camps, they automatically drag out of bed those who feel safe because they are working for the German army.

The thought that tomorrow she's being sent away on the transport begins to grow on Daniella. Though when Harry was deported she stopped caring about what might happen to her. Funny. Here, in the militia compound, you suddenly get homesick for the shoe shop, for the pile of old clothes, for little Bella crawling on all fours in and out of Hayim-Idl's "villa." You miss the ghetto misery which you'd already grown used to; the rickety bed you've left behind, empty, at the Centre. All at once everything seems so terribly near, so intimate.

Vevke must have rushed up to the Centre and is now pacing helplessly among the vacant beds. There's not a thing he can do now. He can't go out while curfew is on. First thing tomorrow he'll probably wait there in the corridor on tenterhooks for curfew to end, so he can rush out to intervene for her. Doubt it will do any good.

IV

The girls are lined up, six abreast. They are to be led out of the ghetto. On the main street of the Aryan quarter the trolleys are waiting to take them to the Dulag.

The faces of the girls, who but a moment ago felt so sure of themselves, suddenly fall. From the Dulag hardly anyone ever gets back. The Dulag is the last stop-over between the ghetto and mysterious death.

Countless files of girls, ranks six abreast move through the dead of night, cordoned by blue-white caps and cocked Gestapo machine guns ready to shoot if a foot should slip out of line. The last ghetto hovels peer at them with dimmed windows. Behind the windows hide heads of dear ones, afraid to look out as they lead off their sisters, their daughters.

The trolleys are ready. A Polish conductor stands by at each throttle. Their whole bearing bespeaks indifference. Evidently, they are used to such midnight jaunts. Their faces are dull, impassive. Hard to tell what they're thinking. Maybe they are wondering how there's room for such a slue of people in the cramped ghetto. Day and night they're taking these people to the Dulag, and the Jewish ghetto there never runs dry. Or maybe they are annoyed: because of these damned Jews they have to drive trolleys now, in the middle of the night. If not for the Jews, they could be at home peacefully asleep with wife and kids.

The trolleys are jammed with girls. Girls standing on the floor, on the benches, pressed into each other. Impossible to pull out a hand. The straps from the ceiling sway empty, to and fro, to and fro. Militiamen guard the sealed car doors. Each is responsible for the "heads" in the car. After a few stops Dreiser's tailor-shop workers hop on to the trolley platforms. They are on the way home from the first night shift. Terror shows in their eyes:

A girls' Aktion!

Coming home they're liable to find that a sister of theirs is already at the Dulag. The heart is sick. They can't wait to step into the house, yet fear wants to put off the moment of coming face to face with the calamity at home. The faces of the crammed girls inside the cars blur. The returning workers look at the girls but do not see them. Before the eyes hovers the face of a sister.

Through the door panes the girls look at the Jews now riding home, the way those sentenced to hanging in the ghetto look at the bystanding Jews whom the Gestapo had ordered to come and witness the execution.

At the sealed door of the trolley stands "13." A Hamburg-born Jew-Militiaman, whose nickname alone spells terror in the ghetto. "13"! He has the number 13 on his blue-white cap. He is the crown and glory of the Jew-Militia. They know him even at Gestapo Headquarters. It's common knowledge: once "13" has been ordered to turn in a "head," the order will be carried out to a "t," with German punctiliousness. He speaks pure Gestapo Germanese, and revels in it. He himself is a refugee from Germany. His hair is cropped, true German style. He wears a brown leather jacket and high officer's boots. His face is bloated, rubicund, and his eyes are bleary and bloodshot from constant bibbing. Whenever the Judenrat has to find a Jew marked by the Gestapo for hanging, leave it to "13" to find him, no matter how well he hides out. Now "13" is in charge of the sealed trolley. Seems the Gestapo is taking special care with this transport: the job was assigned to "13." He stands close upon one of the girls, manœuvres to embrace her, pushes his beery red face at her and presses his body up against her. The girl tries to break loose from him. She wants to squeeze back into the thick-pressed mass—but cannot. She can't even avert her face from him. And "13" talks directly into the fear in her eyes in his pure Germanese:

"*Pass mal auf!*[1] If you knew where you're being taken now, you wouldn't be so hoity-toity."

He presses the girl closer, bends his whole body over her and hurls the words into her:

[1] *Pass mal auf:* watch it.

84

"German soldiers will teach you to push off men's embracing arms. *Pass mal auf*, my kitten!"

The dangling straps swayed empty from the ceiling, to and fro, to and fro. Daniella edged back into the pressing mass of girls' bodies. The trolley rode on, but she didn't feel it. The words hammered inside her temples with terrifying monotony:

"*German soldiers will teach you!*" "*German soldiers will teach you!*"

8

UPON his transfer from Camp Sakrau to Camp Niederwalden, Harry suddenly found himself a "physician."

Against the background of the labour camp, the whole matter of the "sick bay" seemed like a toy in the hands of a maniac. The room was two by nothing and to begin with was set up as a whim of the Camp Commander, so he could brag to the Kameraden in the nearby labour camps: in his camp he has a sick bay! The only bed in the room was a crib. The Commander had picked it up some place because it was white. It was the colour that sold him on it. Makes an impression. Just like in a hospital. Even a small glass cabinet had been installed, and on each of the three shelves stood myriad little bottles. First and foremost: bottles! The Camp Commander gets a big kick out of seeing a lot of bottles. Full or empty—it's all the same. The main thing: the little white labels inscribed in Latin.

To Harry it all seemed as though he were dreaming of a dream.

The whole camp was like a phantasmagoric dream. Although the people within it did not sense it. They were incapable of sensing it. They moved through the camp, as over the surface of the labour area, both on their march-out at dawn and on their march-in at dusk, like creatures whose will had been completely drained from their veins without their being aware when and how it was done to them. Like hollow men; empty containers bobbing at sea. They went where they were taken and stood where they were put. Like inert train cars that continue rolling down the lines after the locomotive has been detached. To a stop. Death drew its curtain over their eyes. Eyes which were already unseeing, but only reflected everything around them with the sheen of dead glass.

But as medic, Harry was comparatively well off and his senses were fully capable of clearly seeing and feeling the horror of the dream about him. And viewing himself in the sick bay, and all the rest of it as a whole against the general backdrop of the labour camp—he felt he was dreaming a dream-within-a-dream.

He, of all people, had been chosen by fate. Queer. He can't remember ever having been a pusher, ever having sought the limelight, ever having sought to attract attention. Not in fantasy, nor in real life. Never. His close friend, Henry Baum the painter, once told him, "You know, Harry, you don't have elbows. But that's all right. You have wings which will carry you much further than those who elbow their way through . . ." Strange that the same thing should happen to him even here, in the other world, in the German labour camp. True, before the war he had begun to study medicine. He liked the profession. But then, there are doubtless many like him at camp, some even graduate doctors, who bit by bit are spitting up their tortured souls on the Baustelle.[1]

His first day here, on returning from the Baustelle at dusk with the labour platoon, the Camp Commander called him out of the ranks by name, and sizing him up from head to toe then and there dubbed him: Physician.

"Physician! We'll build a sick bay in our camp. . . ."

Well, what was he supposed to say to that? First of all, on the march-in from the Baustelle it had already become clear to him that a few more such days and he'll come back a corpse on somebody's shoulders. Besides, the Camp Commander's tone of voice didn't seem to call for any comment on his part which might disappoint His Excellency and the upshot of which would be—immediate death by flogging.

And he wanted very much to live.

God in heaven is his witness that he's ashamed to look the prisoners in the face. It's hard for him to meet their glances at dawn when they march off to the Baustelle and in the evening when they come back. Before it's even dawn, after roll call, they are marched out to the Baustelle, a march which is as good as walking to their death, while he—he heads for the toy room. In the evening they come back

[1] Baustelle (pronounced *Baushteller*): labour area.

86

bearing the day's kill on their shoulders, line themselves up on the assembly ground and wait for roll call. While he, the Physician, who also has to stand roll call, comes there from the sick bay. From their tattered rags the Baustelle breathes like fang marks of a beast on the shredded garment of its victim. God is his witness that he feels ashamed in their presence. He knows he's no better than they. By what right does he sit idle in the camp all day? What makes him different from them? By right, they should loathe him, shun him with disgust. But it isn't so. Just the reverse. They look up to him like cowering dogs, with veneration: The Physician! They are lined up for noon soup and see him go right to the head of the line, come back from the window with a brimming bowl of soup in each hand—and their veneration mounts. It stands to reason: the Physician shouldn't stand in line with all the others. The Physician is a V.I.P. He has his own private room. He doesn't get flogged, doesn't go out to the Baustelle, isn't as tattered as they. He's no common riffraff like them.

As he passes them with the two bowls of soup in his hands, someone in the line risks the question, "Mr. Physician! When is it all right to come in to have a foot bandaged?"

"Any time you feel like it," Harry replies.

The questioner's eyes light up. He is pleased. He got out of the question all in one piece. With the Jew-Chief or with the Kapo[1] you never know when instead of an answer you'll get a tooth knocked out or a kick in the crotch. But not the Physician. To him you can talk. The questioner feels good. He is elated. His face beams: first of all, he's on the soup line—his twenty-four-hour-a-day dream is about to come true. Secondly, he has just completed a successful conversation with one of the camp *élite*. Out of the dismal abyss, luck has flashed him a smile—and he is beatified.

Odd. Of all of them, fate had chosen him to go on being alive even in the camp. He doesn't understand it. His looks may have had something to do with it. The Commander fusses with him and pretties him up as if he were an item belonging to the sick bay. He even brought him a white linen coat, which must have been taken from a new arrival.

"Physician! Fix yourself a white smock from this, and let everyone see there's a physician in camp!"

Another time, the Commander brought him a red sash.

[1] Kapo: labour overseer.

"Physician! Sew yourself a red cross on your sleeve. A big cross, so it will stand out."

During roll call, he stands apart from the rest. Even the Jew-Chief has to line up among the others. Not to mention the Kapo and the rest of the functionaries. But the Physician in his white smock, with the big red cross on the sleeve, stands apart. He is the prince among the camp nobility. Everyone marches to the Baustelle. Many of them will come back dead on their fellows' shoulders. At the evening roll call many will lie on the ground, in a separate row, alongside the first row. They'll count the living, add up the corpses arranged on the ground: all present and accounted for.

Everyone marches to work, while he goes back into his sick bay. Fate must have marked him out for herself.

In the medicine cabinet the bottles are arrayed in even rows. But on the table, too, there are bottles. It's prettier this way. More impressive. The table has a glass top, on which stand jars of all varieties with medicaments of every sort. Many of the transportees took medicines along with them when they set out on their trip. Mothers' hands had packed them in with tears, wrapped them in white cloth and given them to their children heading for the German labour camp: "It'll come in handy if, God forbid, you scratch your finger at work."

Whenever a new transport arrives, the Camp Commander comes striding into the sick bay with the good news:

"Physician! A real haul for the sick bay. Go to it!"

In the corner of the block,[1] where arrivals are searched for the last time, there lie on the floor, off to the side, bandages, gauze, cotton, iodine, valerian, ichthyol, boric acid, zinc ointment, calcium pills, aspirin, pills for constipation and diarrhœa—a real haul for the sick bay.

Upward of a thousand human bodies which, like stuffed dummies, you do not know what's inside them, and you can't get to know what propels them forward still; their whole being motivated by one will, "Eat!"; their lacerated bodies festering with gangrenes as big as the belly, as big as the back—sores to which they have become used as one grows used to polish on manicured nails. Overnight they swell like barrels. Now what: can't pull the pants up the legs. Stark naked they march out to the Baustelle, their jackets tied around their genitals. Their bloated nakedness glistens against

[1] Block: barrack.

88

the clear sky like an inflated toy balloon. But oh, the privy parts are covered.

"Tahitians!" the Germans snicker.

"Tarzans, forward march!"

And the "balloons" march forward to work.

Overnight they suddenly shrivel again to long, scraped bones. You don't know how and when the miracle came to pass. You don't recognize them in their skeletonness, just as you didn't recognize them in their swollenness. Their human semblance has long since been obliterated, as routed out with a plane. Even the identifying marks that distinguish one body from the others are completely blurred by now.

"Physician! A real haul for the sick bay. Go to it!"

On the glass top of the white-lacquered table, more and more toys move in: shiny aluminium boxes, fancy made-in-Germany medicine bottles, spools of adhesive tape. The empty boxes mustn't be thrown away. Were the Physician to do so, he'd have to answer for it with his life. A chart hangs on the wall, on which is entered, with German punctiliousness, each and every addition to the collection. On the table everything must be aligned just so: large with large, small with small, measured and sorted by height and by width: *Order! Symmetry! Discipline! Let's have a good show!*

The steel-gleaming surgical instruments are the Camp Commander's favourites. They were sent to him by the Service Corps HQ personnel as a gift for the sick bay. They, too, must be arrayed on the glass top according to category and size—a precise, even row: the tweezers, pincers, scalpels, and one-sixteenth of an inch between each instrument and the next.

If it were possible to let at least one of the people rest in the sick bay for just one single day—not, God forbid, in the white crib! What a preposterous idea. Everyone knows that the white crib was put in the sick bay solely and exclusively as a show-piece. It is not to be touched! But if at least they'd let someone lie on the floor for a day, it would do him more good than all the best medicine in the world. But it's prohibited to be sick in the camp. That is why the Commander set up the sick bay, so everybody should be healthy.

In the evening, after work, a long line winds before the sick bay door. Those who can still feel hunger sucking away at their life's blood line up for the doctor after they have swallowed the watery soup and have licked their tin plate inside and out. But those who take their soup ration out of sheer reflex—they no longer line up for the doctor, though their body be threadbare as a shredded floor rag; it no longer bleeds blood, anyway. They crawl up into their hutches and wait there to hear again the waking gong, when they will again file off to the Baustelle. They don't even know if night has passed meanwhile; don't feel whether they slept or didn't sleep. It's a sort of continuation whose beginning is beyond recall and whose end is not in sight. It's the Mussulman[1] phase, during which things no longer register in the mind, but are only reflected in the glassiness of the eyes.

Eyes, the setting of whose own life only mirrors itself in them, at a distance.

Often, when the bedtime gong is heard, they come crawling down from their hutches, go out of the block and line up on the assembly ground in precise, even rows. As if by command. They think the gong has sounded morning roll call, and they are ready to march out to work. They have to be driven back up into their hutches. And they don't understand. Why the change? They no longer distinguish between the dark of night and the light of day. Their calcified brains clearly heard the knelling of the gong, and they don't understand. Why aren't they marching out to the Baustelle?

In the evening, the sick bay is crowded with naked legs and arms. Legs. Legs of every variety. As if the whole world were made up of nothing but legs. No bodies. Just long, jutting limbs. At times a pair of eyes flickers. The eyes had fallen upon an open box of white salve. The salve recalls —margarine; or cheese. The eyes want to swallow it. To sink in it the naked crags of teeth protruding from the fleshless gum bones. Better move the box further back on the table.

Harry unbandages a swollen leg. The infection has spread in a big circle over the whole width of the leg. It reeks of rotting flesh. The leg exudes a rank heat, as a mound of rubbish whose top layer has only just been removed after a long while. The flesh is brown, as though it had been roasting, porous and nodose as a sponge. But a sponge is quaggy, and this decay is hard as rock. What is he to do? The wicker wastepaper-basket is again already full of chunks of scoured-

1 Mussulmen: prisoners whose bones were all that held them together.

90

out rottenness. Usually there's not much to do. Especially with fingers. It starts with a rotting nail. It branches through the palm, or into a nearby finger. So he amputates the cankerous finger and a few days later the hand gets well. That is, if the prisoner hasn't first had the life knocked out of him by a Kapo at the Baustelle, or the Jew-Chief at camp.

They don't cry out. He lances and probes into the living flesh, as one probes with a knife point down to the core of a rotten fruit. He scrapes and gouges with the scalpel, deeper, deeper. When will he hit bottom? There's no end to it. What is there beyond the swollen rottenness? Is there no bone there at all? Where in a man is the core of life? Here, a man in the chair, his leg slung across Harry's knees. The scalpel delves deeper and deeper, and he sits there as if the leg were not his at all. Tomorrow this very leg will march him out to the Baustelle! The same leg is about to carry him out of the sick bay and up into his hutch. Is this flesh alive, or not? And if not, where in a man is the core of life?

At times someone will sit in the chair, opposite.

"Where does it hurt you?"

He is not swollen—which leaves him nothing more than bones sheathed in yellow, transparent skin. Not a wound on his body. His mouth is open, he wants to speak, but doesn't find his own voice. Like a person suddenly struck blind who grabbles with his hands, he gropes for his own voice and lands nearby. At last he indicates with a finger:

The lashes of his eyes hurt him . . .

In any other camp such a one would at once have got a whack across his hollow skull that would send him rolling out of the sick bay into the electric barbed wire. Who's he trying to kid? It's getting late. Any minute now and the gong will sound bedtime. Outside there's still a long line of patients, and this jokester—the lashes of his eyes hurt . . . He sits and cheeps like a bird. His pupils are frighteningly dilated, filling out his boundless eyes.

What's to be done with him?

The scalpels lie ready on the table—but there's nothing in his body to cut. The ointment jars stand ready—but there's no wound on his body to heal, no matter how hard you look for it. Unless you cook him up a malady. His mouth cheeps, but it appears that it's not his open mouth but his enormous pupils that plead for his life. Before, he was quiet. Two hours on end he stood outside, unheard. But hardly was he seated before the Physician, than he began convulsing as though poisoned. Hard to make out just what he wants. Very feebly he cheeps:

Please, will someone help him shed a tear—he'll feel so much better—he just knows it. Would the Physician please help him to get just this one tear out?

His convulsions gradually subside. The pupils of his eyes dim. He remains sitting in the chair—still, tranquil, extinguished. The lips of his eyelids are yellow, arid as scorched earth.

Here it is, life! Here! Poised on the threshold of his body, like a bird at the portal of its ravaged nest before taking wing. Who is so blind that could not now tangibly see the sheer, naked life of man? It now pauses outside him, as if wanting to cast one last glance at the place it is about to leave, for ever. Who knows how many years it had warmed this nest; how many carefree days it had had there, how much pain and anguish? But for all the pain and anguish, it remained true to the walls of its abode and would on no account forsake them. Now this body sits there—a desolate, charred ruin. Life turns to go its way, like a humiliated, banished bride.

To the sick bay had he come. Two hours stood in line. It had given him no rest. Please, would the Physician help make it possible for him to cry.

Is there a man alive who will ever know how vast was the pain in his parched eyelashes?

He had felt the moment drawing near. He knew he must give up his chaste bride. She was leaving him. But before their parting, he hurried to the sick bay for help in bringing out a tear from his eyes. He wanted to offer this tear to his departing life as a farewell bouquet of white roses.

But where, in the German camp, at the last moment, are you to get a tear? When the bones are desiccated, the blood vessels empty. A tear. In his last moment—a tear! Who could now get him a tear?

Hippocrates of Concentration Camp Universe! Prescribe this patient a remedy. There will be need for it yet.

"Block orderlies! Carry this corpse out behind the block! Don't forget to report it immediately to the Jew-Chief. Tomorrow, at roll call, the numbers must check."

II

Outwardly, Camp Niederwalden looks different from the other labour camps all over the area. The other camps are usually hidden in a forest, in wooden barracks set up especially for this purpose, surrounded by high-tension barbed wire. The Germans live in stone houses outside the barbed wire perimeter and guard the camps. Camp Niederwalden, on the other hand, is situated among a group of stone houses at the end of a German village, in a tremendous block, which apparently had been a fire house, or a cinema, or maybe both—for at one end of the block the traces of a stage are still discernible, and on either side of the stage is a cubicle, one now serving as sick bay and the other as the Jew-Chief's office.

The huge block is unlit and filled to the rafters with three tiers of wooden bunks. In these hutches the prisoners sleep and live. At the other end of the block is the kitchen, where the soup and bread rations are distributed through a little window. The kitchen is off limits to the prisoners, for its other side borders on the stair vestibule of the German Quarters. The block and parade ground in front of it are ringed with barbed wire and watch towers. Only the side of the camp facing the village is blocked off by a high stone wall netted with veins of barbed wire, looking like a villa wall veined with late-autumn creepers.

During the day, when every one is at the Baustelle, Harry paces among the hutches in the dark, vacant block. In what way can he help them? He knows the hell they're going through at the Baustelle, though he was out there with them only one day. And he still remembers only too well the Baustelle at Camp Sakrau. Nor has he forgotten how he had stood on the sick line there pleading for them to bandage his punctured, pus-dripping palms—palms in which he had to grip the heavy pickaxe and smash away at the rocky hillside the day long without let-up, without a break.

"Blow, whoreson! There are no bandages for such stinking little holes! Blow and bust, whoreson!" Goldmann, the medic at Sakrau, screeched at him.

If he hadn't run for it right then and there, he'd have got Goldmann's boot right between the legs.

Before, when pacing among the bunks during the day, Harry would fluff up the straw in their hutches so they'd have it softer at night. What else could he do for them? The salves were all used up. No bandages left. What else could he do for them besides fluff up their straw?

But today, the Camp Commander happened to catch him at it and flared up very indignantly, "Hey! What do you think you're doing there? A fine job for a physician! I never! Put on your white smock and back to your medicines! I'll teach them tonight how they're to make beds for me!"

He's really messed things up. He wanted to help them, and has only made it harder on them. The poor wretches don't know what they're in for when they get back to camp this evening. He's really cooked their goose.

In the sick bay everything is spick and span. Harry is depressed and heavy hearted. On the table, the empty bottles are arrayed in straight rows along the wall. The upstretched necks of the bottles claw at his brain. They bristle like bayonet points, spring out of the neat rows, up and down, up and down, and stab under his scalp.

The wicker wastepaper-basket near the leg of the table now gapes empty. A sheet is spread in the crib—white, smooth, without the slightest wrinkle. The two chairs stand at the table precisely where they should—one for the physician, one for the sick Mussulman. Stillness.

He takes a chair, draws it to the wall, climbs on to it, and looks out of the high heavily iron-barred lattice.

He can only see the hinges on the civilians' entrance in the corner of the compound. A lone sapling stands by the heavy stone wall which seals off the camp with its back, brute and scaly, like a crouching monster's.

Whenever he looks at this tender tree a gnawing sadness grips him, often so oppressive that he can't breathe. He forgets he is himself a prisoner here. It hurts him to see the wall looming over the tender sapling with its hideous back, blocking it off from the world. He can feel the tree choking, its mouth agape, gasping for air, for breath. It wants to breathe . . . to breathe . . .

Here, from behind the lattice bars, the civilians' gate isn't visible. As though it had been planned that way, so no prisoner should ever again see the likeness of a free man. A strip of earth below; a strip of sky above; a grim, brooding wall stretching opposite the lattice; barbed coils of wire above the wall piercing the naked blueness of the sky, like rusty threads stitching it fast to the wall of the camp.

He's put seven skin-boiled potatoes in three of the block bunks today: three in Tedek's, two in Zanvil Lubliner's, and two in architect Weisblum's. A peaked lump protrudes from one of Tedek's three potatoes. The potato skin is white as alabaster; enticing, provoking to distraction. *The lump!* He could just bite into it. Just the lump, no more. With the tip of his tongue he'd push it in between gum and cheek and leave it there for a whole hour. For a whole hour he'd suck and swallow its juicy spit. No! He won't go near there! He mustn't dare touch the potatoes! It always starts this way: a nibble . . . another nibble . . . First from a potato of Tedek's, then from a potato of the architect's, until he loses control altogether. The animal in him stirs, he goes completely berserk and pounces on the nibbled potatoes and bolts them down. No! Today he will not do it. In any case he won't be able to keep the nip in his mouth for a whole hour. It melts in the mouth within a few seconds. No sooner is it in his mouth than his tongue coils and reaches into the cache up in his mouth. A few such licks and the nip is gone. No! It's just an excuse. Today he will not allow himself to do it. Today he won't go near the potatoes. Not even to look at them. He must control himself. He put them there himself, didn't he? Then let them lie there. Taboo. Let him imagine he's already eaten them. Well, would that make him any fuller?

Two days after he was named medic, Tedek showed up in the sick bay. Harry didn't recognize Tedek, but Tedek recognized him. Tedek had been sent here before Harry, from Johannesdorf labour camp. If Tedek weren't one of the sons —"The Five Oaks"—of Vevke the cobbler, he would long since have perished in Johannesdorf; and if not there, then here, at Niederwalden, like all the others who came on his transport, not a trace of whom was left. What good will his support do him now? What's there left to do for him now? It's much too late. True, he steals a piece of bread off his own ration every day to give Tedek along to the Baustelle, and every day lets him have a few spoons of his soup; and once a week, when it's skin-boiled potatoes instead of soup, Harry stows several potatoes away in Tedek's bunk for him

95

to eat when he gets back from the Baustelle, so that in the morning he'll be able to take along his bread ration, whole, to the Baustelle. But is there any chance that all this will do him any good?

Weird. There's no identifying today's Tedek with the old Tedek, of the ghetto. Not the slightest resemblance. That one had a wise thoughtful face, a fine face, etched with determination. *This man knows what he's about, and is sure to get there.* How identify that Tedek with this hollowed-out head of today? What happened to the substance that had once filled it? How does a man's head become so idiotically empty, so totally vacuous that the sheer sight of him evokes horror?

Take Zanvil Lubliner. In the ghetto he was as simple a Jew as they come, a small-time tailor. Match him up with Tedek now; the same appearance, the same face, except that one is fifty and the other is only twenty—both looking like shrivelled boys of fifteen. But when Zanvil opens his mouth, you immediately know that this was once a human being. Torture-racked, battered and scourged, true, but nonetheless a human being. In spite of everything—still Zanvil.

But Tedek—intelligent, able Tedek, Daniella's chum—an idiot! What's at the root of it? How does it come about?

Toward evening, when Tedek returns from work, Harry immediately leads him into the sick bay, washes him, bandages his sores and seats him in a corner. Here, at least, he'll be safe from the beatings—both of the block orderlies and of the block chief, as well as from all the rest of the treatment awaiting a prisoner in the block. After sick call, he sits with him and talks to him as to a sick child. At first, Tedek would tell him all that happened to him from the day he first met Daniella until the day he got here. This way Harry learned many details of Daniella's life in the ghetto that she had kept secret from him. But hearing Tedek tell of those days and of his innermost feelings towards Daniella makes Harry shudder. The most sacred and intimate memories now come out of Tedek's mouth as from a hollowed-out idiot-head. He blubbers, and his eyes are fixed on Harry's bread ration showing from the medicine cabinet. His own ears don't hear the words he speaks. The intelligent, handsome face of the old Tedek now bespeaks one single bovine insight: "If he gets a piece of bread, he'll go on telling." Or: "If he keeps telling, he's bound to get a piece of bread."

As the cow knows that those who milk her are duty-bound to fill her trough with hay.

And Tedek had loved Daniella with all his youthful ardour. He had given his life for her. Where is that steely look of his eyes? What has happened to all that once throbbed and teemed inside that brilliant head of Tedek's?

On one of the shoots of the sapling by the wall dangles a solitary leaf. The leaf flutters monotonously in the wind, back and forth, back and forth—as if a secret power were relentlessly whipping it on—a quivering, shimmering greenness.

No! He won't give in to any vile thoughts! He won't go anywhere near the potato. Thank God the worst is over. The worst of it is when you get the ration. You start eating, hunger scorches your inside like fire, and you have to put some aside for those for whom you owe it to provide. They are worked mercilessly at the Baustelle, while you amble idly about the camp, and get two rations of soup into the bargain. It's a crime even to think of going near the hutches —only to *look* at the potatoes, you tell yourself. If you had the guts to resist the potatoes when you got them, then you should have the stamina to hold out now that you've put them where they belong.

Strange thing, that. At the Baustelle you don't feel the hunger this badly. At the Baustelle time passes much faster. In Sakrau, where he, too, had worked at the Baustelle, he never felt such excruciating hunger as today, hanging around the camp doing nothing. At the Baustelle you get weak, you want to faint, but fear doesn't let you faint. The fear of the vicious blows offsets the pains of hunger. But this day-long aimless meandering about, that's when hunger is almost unbearable. It drives you frantic the way it wrings and sucks at your guts. You wish you could go insensible, but you can't. In spite of yourself you hold on to your senses.

And whose share does he think he's going to touch?— never. Not Tedek's three potatoes! Tedek is his own flesh and blood. Tedek—is Daniella.

And Zanvil—though he doesn't demand in so many words —his two potatoes are sacred. May he choke on them, if he so much as touches Zanvil's potatoes. This man has a special place in his heart yet since their days together at Schwecher's tailor shop. It's been a long time since he's given anything to Zanvil. For many days now he's been trying with all his will power to withhold something for him—but he just can't do it. He just can't bring himself to it. He really can't look him in the eye any more. Zanvil probably thinks he's forgotten him—

No. Architect Weisblum is Sanya's friend. Putting the two potatoes away for the architect fills him through and through with a holy tremor, as though he were touching with his body the memory of Sanya. Day in day out the architect stands near the sick bay, doggedly watching Harry's every step: maybe he'll get something. Impossible to pass him without seeing his cadging, demanding look. It hurts to see the architect in this state. It's an insult to Sanya's memory. The architect apparently realizes it. He knows Harry's weak spot and takes advantage of it. He follows him with the cringing, fawning look of a beaten cur. If he touches the architect's two potatoes now, who knows when he'll again be able to give him anything? "Tomorrow. That's it—tomorrow," he always kids himself; keeps putting it off from one day to the next. Maybe it's because the architect demands it, as though he had it coming to him—

Howls of laughter and drunken shouts carry from the German Quarters. They break in through the wooden kitchen door, roll down the long block, into the sick bay, and go shrilling into Harry's eardrums.

Usually, when he hears the boisterous din from the German Quarters, he scampers up into a third-tier bunk and hides there in the dark. Better be careful. Never know what you may be in for during a German orgy. In Sakrau, the drunken Germans got hold of the Jew-Chief—a handsome young fellow from Berlin—during one of their carousals, and before the prisoners returned from the Baustelle in the evening, had tossed him back into the block—strangled, nude, his whole body a mess of blue spots.

The sapling by the wall is weighted down with boiled potatoes. Before his eyes—a blur of potatoes. Every leaf—a potato. Can't tear the eyes away from them. And in the centre of the solitary shoot dangles the big potato with the peaked lump, the one hidden in Tedek's hutch. The potato pirouettes before him with special seductiveness, beckoning and tantalizing beyond endurance. But all at once the peaked lump takes on the shape of Tedek's head, his facial expression on returning from the Baustelle. And as he looks,

Daniella's blue eyes look beseechingly at him through the sockets of Tedek's skeleton-head. A head from within a head. As though Tedek's head were of yellow glass, transparent. And the heads slowly emerge from each other and stand side by side, just as he used to see them linked, arm in arm, in the sunlight of Hayim-Idl's plot—

The "plot." Summertime in the ghetto. The Judenrat parcelled out the land between the various Jew-Quarters into many plots to be cultivated by the Jews. These plots—zhalkes, as they were called—were available for sub-leasing by any Jew. But, at first, there weren't many takers. "Before we ever see a ripe tomato the war'll end, and our money will be down the drain. Oh, no! It's just some more monkey business cooked up by the Judenrat gang to swindle us out of our money!" the Jews contended.

Hayim-Idl, ever obsessed with the one idea that his "villa" must never go hungry, immediately latched on to a plot. Just for the devil of it. "We've got so many felts stowed away, let's stow away a zhalke!" he shouted into his wife's deaf ear. It goes without saying that Hayim-Idl didn't have the time or the mind for "agriculture," nor did he know just how you go about getting the earth to produce a tomato or a red radish. And so it was that Daniella became Hayim-Idl's sharecropper.

Those were the loveliest days of the ghetto. Then, it almost seemed possible to forget everything happening about them. The black, soft-pleated earth, the warm earth, soaked into its bosom the brow's sweat together with ghetto tears. The sky stretched free and boundless overhead. Together Daniella and Tedek spaded the soil, seeded and watered it, and together enjoyed the fruit of their toil. Ruddy radishes, green peas in their pods, tomatoes, tiny potatoes.

Yes. Those were the loveliest days of the ghetto.

Like the succulent tomato glowing in the flush of its ripeness against the sun, unmindful of the ghetto soil at which it suckles, so Daniella and Tedek forgot the world closing in on them like a noose. To them, Hayim-Idl's plot was like a sweet dream which the angel of dreams will sometimes grant the doomed man in his death cell on his life's last night—compensation for the sunrise he'll never again see.

Every Sunday Harry would come to them at Hayim-Idl's zhalke. They would sit on the stone bench—Tedek's handiwork—and Daniella would stuff Harry's pockets with the produce of her plot, as a gift for Sanya. And as Harry made his way back to his Jew-Quarter, he would turn his face to them from afar and see them linked together, head to head, radiant in the sunshine, seeing him off with their glances. From afar, Hayim-Idl's plot suddenly seemed like a lone piece of wreckage on a sea of floating icebergs. He abruptly lowered his eyes, turned around and hurried on to his Jew-Quarter.

Now, looking at the peak-lumped potato beckoning to him from the sapling, enticing him to the brink of madness, he again sees the heads of Daniella and Tedek linked motionless in the sun, seeing him off.

What is Daniella doing now? His heart skips a beat; how is Daniella getting on? Good thing she works at the Labour Commissioner's shoe shop. That's a safe nook. And all thanks to Vevke, Tedek's father. A remarkable person this Vevke. Good thing there are still such people around. Daniella is in good hands. Nothing to worry about. Sanya also works in a good shop. Wilderman's is considered one of the safest shops. And then, her cousin Bianca is supervisor there. That should make it a lot easier for her. Sanya saw what was coming and quickly got herself transferred from Schwecher's shop to Wilderman's. It's clear now she acted wisely. Nothing to worry about, really. Tonight he'll save a whole soup ration for Tedek. Then Tedek will be able to take the three potatoes to the Baustelle tomorrow. Every day he'll give Tedek a whole soup. Share and share alike. It's settled: a soup every day. How could he have thought of—

"Yaga! Yaga!"

The voice burst in through the lattice from the direction of the German Quarters. He looked up and saw a beautiful blonde woman standing motionless and gazing at him. She is wearing a woman's military uniform, a garrison cap cocked on her platinum-blonde curls, and a dark leather knout tucked, cavalry style, under her arm. How long can she have been standing there like this, looking at him?

This must be the German woman who comes to the Camp Commander. His lover. How did she suddenly crop up there, by the wall? How hadn't he noticed her when she parked herself there to watch him? She stands there motionless, looking him straight in the eyes. He gripped the bars as though about to back away from the lattice. But her un-blinking gaze seemed to rivet him to the spot. His disappearance from the lattice now would be like a direct insult at her. Like not acknowledging a greeting, though the greeter looks straight at you.

From across the parade ground they kept calling: "Yaga! Yaga!" But the woman didn't stir. Shoulder leaning against the wall, she went on standing there, deaf to the shouts directed at her, her eyes fastened on him. She must have sensed that he'd already seen her.

Harry felt all the ridiculousness and danger fraught in this moment. His head was inserted in one of the lattice squares, like a head portrait inside an iron frame.

It lasted a split second. Maybe longer. He couldn't go on standing there this way. He tore himself away from the lattice and jumped off the chair. The sick-bay door stood open. The aisle between the wooden bunks tapered off into the darkness of the block. He didn't know whether to shut the door, or leave it open.

Her voice reached him from outside the lattice.

"Jew! Don't be frightened! Let me look at you some more."

He knew he didn't belong to himself. It suddenly struck him: what if she comes into the sick bay? What if the Germans follow her in! This he must avert. At once. Only not the Germans! No telling how such a visit is liable to turn out.

He went back up the chair to the lattice.

Now she was standing by the lattice. He saw the olive drab of her SS uniform. Her full, round, white cheeks made him giddy. He had long since forgotten that such a form was still to be found on a human being. In the ghetto once, he happened to find a piece of pre-war bread. The whiteness of the bread had made his eyes smart. He couldn't look at the bread. He couldn't imagine that there had ever been such white bread to eat. With both hands she pressed the knout across her thighs. At the end of the whip gleamed a small steel bullet.

She asked, "What are you doing in camp in the middle of the day?"

"I'm the camp medic," he said.

He stood behind the lattice. She lifted her eyes to him and mumbled as though to herself:

"Like Holy Christ . . . Lord, the face of Holy Christ . . ."

Drunken German ribaldry carried from the other side of the parade ground, "Yaga! Yaga! Where are you?"

She turned, started moving off toward the voices, then immediately swung her face around to the lattice, and with worshipful eyes, transported in ecstasy, whispered:

"Lord . . . that face . . . the face of Holy Christ . . ."

9

WHEN the transport of girls reached the Dulag, the building was vacant. The three-storey Dulag building, always overflowing with captured Jews, this time stood completely deserted. As if the Germans had cleared it especially for tonight's girl-Aktion.

Over the door of the assembly hall flickered a small kerosene lamp, barely showing the rungs of the ladder leading to the upper level of sleeping boards which extended over the whole length of the hall, dividing it in two and doubling its capacity.

Tens of thousands of people had already lain there on the sparse straw, before their deportation. Here was the last stop before crossing over to that other obscure world. Rivers of tears had already flowed here, but the Dulag had the capacity to absorb human woe like an abyss never to be sated.

The girls clambered up on to the boards, threw themselves on the straw, and one by one were engulfed by the darkness. No one spoke a word. Each was encased within herself—those in whom there was still a faint warm stirring of hope as well as those already numb with despair. The boards were crammed with lying bodies; yet each could deem herself here unutterably alone, forsaken for all time.

No one spoke a word. As though the heart were afraid that the mouth would let fall what was about to happen. Each was now in communion with those mourning her in the ghetto. Beloved faces hovered before the eyes. They could hear their weeping, reach out the arms to embrace them, hug them close for none to separate. The arms ached to be stretched out to them, but in the haunting stillness of the Dulag every limb was afraid to let out the least stir. The fear of a fear unknown.

The night oozed out its last black drop.

II

A new day began to whiten the squares of the barred window bisected by the board layer—half a window for the upper level of the hall, half for the lower level. The girls did not raise their heads, as if wishing to avert the glance of the new day, as if wishing it would let them lie here this way for ever. But the new day went on its rounds. It peered through the barred half-windows like a day guard come to relieve the night watch, ran its eyes over the straw as though taking count of the bodies it is about to take into its purview, contemplated them through eyes slowly opening into an evil glint. Its glance crept along the walls into the deepest, darkest corners to see them all, to make sure that none escape its designs mapped out for them beforehand.

One by one the heads started up. Each looked at her neighbour, and the sight of the other brought the realization that it was they—all together and each of her own—who were the central figures in this Aktion. The Dulag and the whole night-Aktion had been set up exclusively for them.

Eyes searched about for a familiar face. Those who during the night had no place to lie now sat propped against the wall, heads hunched over updrawn knees, staring mutely at those lying on the straw.

Daniella sat leaning against the wall. Will Vevke succeed? It would have been much easier for him to get her out of the militia. From the militia building people do sometimes get out. But hardly ever from the Dulag. She's never heard of such an instance herself, except for the big-wig "screw-turners," whom the Judenrat itself gets out of the Dulag. Vevke will head right over to the Judenrat. No question about that. He'll intervene for her. But will it do any good? Wishful thinking! He can't afford a bribe. And besides, she sees who's lying here: girls more important than herself; girls who strutted about in the ghetto all frilled and rouged up; girls who were in with the Judenrat and the militia—every last one of them is now lying here on the straw, right along with those who had slaved at the "war-essential" shops. Slim chance Vevke'll be able to get the Judenrat to save her out of all the others.

The women will all be coming to work soon in the rag

room. They'll see she's missing. They'll hear that during the night she'd been taken away in the girl-Aktion. Many will feel sorry for her—and go on picking from the clothes heap. After breakfast she'll be all but forgotten. It's always that way. You hear that during the night a neighbour, an acquaintance, or just somebody who had only yesterday been working with you was dragged out of bed; you hear—and in a little while you've forgotten all about it. The feeling that the shadow of your own "I" is still moving about the ghetto blots out and makes you forget everything around you, as though the very forgetting were a sure charm against your being taken from the ghetto . . . If only she knew it's to Harry's camp they're sending her, she'd go there gladly. Just their being together would give them strength to stand up to the worst hardships. Harry was looking sick lately. He never complained, never even let her mention it, but she could plainly see he was very sick. How will he ever be able to take the brutal grind at the camp? At least if they were at the same camp, they might be able to help each other along. Maybe they have shops there, like in the ghetto. She would help him at work. She's healthier and stronger than he, even if he did consider her a baby right up to the last.

Where are they going to send her? The worst of it is just not knowing. There's no way of finding out where they send people from here. Where are those labour camps? What kind of shops do they have there? People would give anything for an inkling of where their relatives have been sent and what they are doing there. But not all the money in the world can get them this information. Neither from the Judenrat nor from the militia. Maybe they don't know either.

Some of the girls crowd to the barred half-window. Outside, the rising day unveils a faraway world belonging not to them. Actually, even yesterday, this world did not belong to them. Yet the heart silently weeps for the dreary ghetto sky which has now also been taken from them, for ever. They look out through the iron squares. Their eyes are dry. But all at once each feels that the heart has eyes, and it is these eyes that now run over with tears.

It is roomier on the straw now. The girls who had been sitting against the wall all night stretch their cramped legs and feel relieved. As if all they lacked here was the pleasure of stretching their legs out on the straw.

Everywhere in the world the ceiling is high. Here, it's impossible to stand upright. The ceiling presses down on the nape. This is the first time she has held a ceiling in her palms. The ceiling and the walls are dotted with tiny words, like a grocery bill jotted on a soiled piece of paper. All sorts of inscriptions and scratchings, topping each other and overlapping one another. A huge mass grave in which the corpses lie strewn all over each other. Those who were here before wanted in this way to leave behind a memorial—the inscription on the Dulag wall.

On the ceiling above her is a symmetrical, skilfully drawn tombstone. In the centre of the tombstone is a Star of David with a tree beside it. The top of the tree lops down, snapped at the trunk. Beneath the tree—a column of names. All almost the same tender age, perhaps classmates. All from the same home town.

A shiver runs through her: maybe she'll find some sign of Harry here too! She searches along the walls, on the ceiling overhead—swarms of inscriptions, tiny and big, plain and flourished, myriad symbols and monograms, in Yiddish, Polish, Hebrew, German. One left on the wall a letter to his brother; a second, a farewell note to his mother; a third, to his sweetheart. One elegizes the long, curly braids of his little daughter which he'll never again see; another begs his father's forgiveness for not having supported him sufficiently in the ghetto. All underscored with one postscript: "Remember to avenge us!"

A sea of names and inscriptions. Names of women and names of men. Such as wrote their testament groupwise, and such as only left their names, singly. An immense cemetery, crammed to overflowing. Each name—a person's life, snuffed out before his eyes. Each name—a tragedy of a man and of man.

She rummages among the inscriptions the way one seeks the body of a relative in a newly unearthed mass grave. The skeletons swirl before the eyes. In any of them you may suddenly recognize your brother.

She gets down on her knees, stares helplessly at the black swarm of dots: an ocean of names, to whose depths Harry's name has sunk without a sound. Gone down, without a ripple, without a trace.

Beyond the halves of the barred window, the Aryan house-tops neighbouring the Dulag come into view—houses in which only Jews once lived. Now Poles live there. The Jews' place is in the Dulag, or in the ghetto—where they wait their turn to the Dulag. Outside, the world sleeps on though the new day has been up for a while. And here, behind the squares of the bisected window—here you look at the new day and you don't remember, you aren't even concerned whether it's a summer day or a winter day, whether it's snowing outside or raining. You just watch the new day coming up and try to guess: what does this day have in store? What is it bringing for those looking out to it from behind the iron bars of the Dulag window?

In the assembly halls of the Dulag, in the corridors, on every storey and staircase, countless girls mill about. Those who were brought here together with her during the night, and those who were brought later, in the morning, from the outlying ghettos in the area. Daniella weaves her way among them from storey to storey, looking for a familiar face. Maybe she'll find something out; they might be calling out the names of those whom the shop exempts from the Dulag. Here you never can tell. Here death limns illusions the way winter dabs frost blossoms on window panes.

By the exit to the compound Daniella catches sight of Fella, standing and talking to a militiaman.

Fella is as chic as ever. It's obvious she didn't spend the night on the filthy straw like all the rest. Her hair is neatly set, not tousled, and there's not a wrinkle in her coat, though her face is not as self-assured and smiling as usual. Daniella stands off. She doesn't want to intrude on Fella's conversation. But Fella notices her, leaves the militiaman and hurries over. A weary bitter smile clouds her sparkling teeth.

"Well, Daniella, so here we are in the Dulag, eh?"

"You don't have any chance of getting out of here either? Why, you're so thick with the militia and your special card was issued by the militia chief himself!" Daniella wonders.

". . . *a card from the militia*," Fella muses. "*So thick.*" How many times did they tell her there: "Fella, your mouth's too big . . ." Or: "One day, Fella, you'll put your foot in your mouth . . ."

"Seems like I've had it," she answers quietly. "If Monyek himself put me on the list, he wants to get rid of me. Looks like he's had his fill of me. . . ."

Daniella feels like saying something; she tries to find the right word to cheer up Fella without humbling her. But Fella cuts in:

"Oh, I'm not calling it quits. I'm not one of those lily livers. I'll tie the score with that Judenrat outfit. They're not sitting home sousing and stuffing their fat guts and sending me to work my heart out for the Germans. They've got another guess coming. I'll give Monyek Matroz something to remember me by. Just wait'll I get out of here. But if it's labour camp in the cards for me, I'll take care of that too. Leave it to me, kid. There's no stopping me till I've got that Monyek by the collar, and then, take it from me, he won't know whether he's coming or going. I'll square it with him for everyone. Just you leave it to me."

There was something about Fella that imbued everyone around her with confidence. Even in the worst predicaments she radiated dogged tenacity and resoluteness. And Daniella, even though she had so far stared death in the face many more times than Fella, felt in her presence like a child clutching at a grown-up's leg when a snarling dog sets upon them on the road. Secretly Daniella now prayed that if she must go to the labour camp it should at least be with Fella. Were Fella to succeed in getting out of the Dulag, Daniella would feel ever so abandoned. Being with Fella makes it easier to stand the fear. Even at the labour camp it will be easier with Fella.

She suddenly felt ashamed at the ugly selfish thought, and in order to shout it down within her she quickly said:

"Fella, you can have my labour card. Maybe it'll help you get out. You have pull, and the German tore up your card . . ."

"You sweet, silly kid! Everybody here's got a labour card. You really figure a labour card's going to do any good here? Innocent little thing that you are!"

"I thought for sure you'd be able to do something with it."

"Oh, they know me only too well here," Fella said, with a wry smile. "They know I never laid eyes on a shop. And how they know! Besides, back at the militia, one of those blue-white soldier boys told me this is a super-strict Aktion. Looks like we're screwed proper."

She hugged Daniella's shoulder silently, devotedly. Arm in arm they went up the steps leading to the assembly halls.

On their way up, Daniella said in a constrained, tear-choked voice, "Fella, let's always stick together—let's never break up—I'm so terribly lonely."

Fella hugged Daniella closer. "Silly, who isn't lonely here?"

III

On the balcony not far from the Dulag, a family sat down to breakfast. The woman filled the cups from a white china kettle, first for the man, then for the others around the table. The kettle gleamed white against the brightness of the day. Daniella stood at the window, her head pressed against the iron bars—

On the pavement of the street facing the Dulag, there suddenly appeared out of nowhere—Vevke.

Up until very recently, Jews were still allowed on these streets around the Dulag. Today it's certain death for a Jew so much as to get near here.

Vevke darts furtive glances up at the Dulag windows. At his feet he has a large basket full of wooden shoe lasts, under the guise that he happens to be passing on his way to the shoe shop. Daniella doesn't know what to do. Vevke is looking right at her, but can't see her because of the thick iron bars. She ran to call Fella.

"Maybe he has some good news. Maybe he's found out something. Must be important. Or he wouldn't be risking his life to come here. But how'll he let me know from so far? How can I signal him?" The words spurted from Daniella.

Fella tries calling, whistling—but it's useless. There's the danger that German guards around the building will notice, and Vevke'll be finished. Vevke fidgets nervously. It's obvious he's on pins and needles. The basket full of lasts stands beside his feet, to make it seem he is pausing there a minute to catch his breath. He looks in all directions to make sure no one sees him, and immediately darts his glance up at the barred Dulag windows. But from so far, he can't possibly make out a face behind the thick bars or hear a guarded call coming from there.

Fella gives up.

"Nothing Vevke can do here. Probably came just to see you. Maybe he wants to tell you goodbye, the fool!"

Daniella's eyes fill with tears. A hot wave sweeps over her heart: *"the fool ..."*

Vevke fidgets on the sidewalk. It's obvious he is nervous, tense, but not ready to give up. Every time a German goes by Vevke snatches the heavy basket up on to his wide shoulders, manipulates it with raised arms on his back, as though trying to find the right position for it. As soon as the German is out of sight, he puts the heavy basket down and again sends his glances groping over the iron-clad windows. Looking. Looking.

Vevke's showing up here by the Dulag fills Daniella's heart with a turmoil of emotions. Tears of painful joy well up in her. At a moment like this it's good to see that someone out there, outside the iron bars, remembers you. So many girls here at the Dulag—privileged characters and bribers—and not one of them has had anybody come to see her. Just she. For a fleeting moment a sense of chosenness engulfs her, and this feeling seems to distil her pain. Even if Vevke only came to see her off, even then she feels elated. But she would like just one thing now: to signal him that she sees him, sees him, and that he'd better hurry up and get away from here. Standing exposed on the street that way he's taking his life in his hands. The basket of lasts is a flimsy excuse during the third degree in the Gestapo dungeon. Why doesn't he get away from here!

If she could at least reach out her hand and give him some kind of signal: she sees him! Please, oh please, would he leave! Though she feels that with his leaving the last thread connecting her with the world will be severed. If only Vevke could go on standing there for ever, so she could see him and see him. This looking at Vevke now sends a quiver of homeness through her, a feeling of father and mother, of family: someone still remembers. If she could just tell him how grateful she is! If there were only some way she could let him know what it means to her and that she'll never forget him for it. But for heaven's sake, let him take off! Quickly. As fast as he can. Let him—

"Down to the compound! Everybody down! Jump to it! Jump to it!"

The shouts carry through all the halls, through every storey, up the stairs, as if to shake the Dulag out of a deep slumber. Militiamen hustle around shouting, "Everyone down! Quicker! Quicker!"

Gestapo and Sipo[1] ring the Dulag compound. The girls fall in by ranks. The Germans count off, call the roll to make sure everyone is present. The lined-up girls tremble. Teeth chatter. Terror envelops the compound, as though the Aktion were only just beginning.

Fella whispers as to herself, "Now the jig's up for sure."

Daniella feels the shudder run through her shoulders: "*Now the jig's up . . .*"

All present and accounted for. Gestapomen unsling their machine guns. Safeties click in unison. They are testing the guns before the girls to make sure they are ready to fire. The smell of something horrid assails the air. Is this the end?

The gate of the Dulag opens wide. Ranks of girls, six abreast, face the gate, ready. Stand and wait. Rigid—

"Forward march!"

Sigh of relief. The fluttering heart doesn't know whether to be happy or to go right on being afraid. No time to decide.

The ranks march.

Where?

To the train, probably.

IV

On the pavements on both sides of the street people were strolling leisurely and carefreely along. Many stopped to watch the "Yiddishers" being led down the middle of the street. They wagged fawning smiles at the Germans girding the girls with the levelled machine guns in their hands.

Once, only Jews lived in these streets. The Jews had built these houses and lived in them. Now, Poles live here—the same Poles who, before the war, had waved their patriotism on high and never let up chanting: "The Jews are selling our Motherland to the enemy!" But no sooner did the Germans come in than these self-same rabid patriots turned overnight into Volksdeutsche.[2] Many of them now sport the Nazi party emblems with pride on their lapels, and in turn each of them was given a Jewish apartment or Jewish business.

Among the marching girls many are daughters of families

[1] Sipo Sicherheitspolizei: Security Police.

[2] Volksdeutsche: German nationals who do not live in but profess allegiance only to Germany.

who had lived in the streets through which they are now being led. Dumbly they lift their eyes to the windows behind which they had lived, to the railings of the balconies on which they had sat. From there, grinning faces of Polish girls look back at them. The eyes of the herded girls rove shamefacedly over the house walls. This is their last goodbye.

These are the houses they were born in. These are the streets they played in as children. Through these gates they skipped off to school every morning. Here stood their cradle. Here they spun their fairytale dreams.

Every brick here is alive with memories. Every tree—a trove of budding girlhood. On more than one tree is carved a heart, pierced with a lover's arrow, beside the initials of a classroom sweetheart.

Under this sky they had grown and they felt toward it what children the world over feel toward their kindred sky.

Now they march over these familiar pavements, surrounded by strangers with levelled machine guns in their hands, whose faces they had never seen; whose honour they had never touched. The strangers are now leading them away from here.

Where?

Why? . . .

Daniella had not lived in these streets. She wasn't born here. To her these windows and balconies didn't speak of sundered home. They only bring back her march, together with her classmates, through the streets of Kongressia. That time, too, there were heads looking out of open windows. But then they were heads of parents, mothers, sisters, youngsters. They were waving white kerchiefs.

"Pleasant trip!"

"Have a good time!"

From a side-street someone comes running out, a basketful of shoe lasts on his shoulders. He edges along the house walls, so as to steer clear of the onlookers enjoying the procession down the middle of the street. His legs wobble along as though buckling under the heavy load on his back. With one upstretched hand he holds the basket by the rim, and with the other hand—open-palmed, fingers outspread—he keeps wiping his downcast face, his nose, his eyes, so the haze of tears will not block his view. The muscles of his neck are tensed, bulging from under the heavy basket like the neck of a horse hauling an overloaded dray. The up-darting glances of the down-pressed head search nervously, furtively rake through the mass of girlish heads marching down the middle of the street.

Daniella struggles to catch his glance. She wants him to see her. She knows it's for her that Vevke is now running after the transport. Maybe he has something important to tell her at the last minute. But what can he say to her now? Something really important? Or maybe he did come only to part with her? "*The fool*." Fella doesn't know Vevke. How can Fella possibly know what kind of person he is? He's looking for her. No! She doesn't dare signal him. She can really bring disaster on him. He is looking for her. She sees it. But his tear-fogged glance just doesn't manage to meet her eyes.

The first ranks were entering the station. Vevke halted near the wall of a house. He did not see her.

Off in the distance, from among the waves of heads, the basket full of shoe lasts looked whitely back at her like the mast of a sinking sailboat.

Vevke didn't see her. What was he going to tell her?

V

On the outside, the train was bedecked with huge German characters:

WHEELS AWAY TO VICTORY!

A long train had been reserved especially for the girls of the night-Aktion. Numerous rails. Locomotives. Heads of firemen bent over their work leer at the lined-up girls, as they go on feeding shovelfuls of coal into the gaping engine furnace. Thick black-white knots of sparkling smoke belch and billow from the smokestacks. WHEELS AWAY TO VICTORY!

. . . Countless locomotives . . . leering faces . . . smokestacks . . . Daniella looks. Her brain swims. Everything doubles. More. More. Tenfold, hundredfold, thousandfold. They're all chasing her. In a minute they'll grab hold of her.

She trembles. She's seen all this before! Exactly, exactly the same, the same locomotives, the same leering faces, the same chilling fear. Everything, everything the same! But she doesn't know whether she saw it in reality and is now having a nightmare, or whether that was the nightmare—

Who is so wise as to fathom the cryptic writing an unseen

hand will from time to time draw on the panels of our dreams?

Germans, men and women, Fräuleins, Reichsdeutsche, Volksdeutsche stream on to the platform, each toward his train—homeward or to business, fancy leather luggage in their hands. On many of the valises the outlines of plucked-off initials of their former owners are still discernible. Some stand and wait for their train, which hasn't come in yet. Others stroll up and down the platform. Mothers buy goodies for their children at the sweets stands. The children are all primped up, with a Hitler bang pasted over the brow.

Freedom! God's most precious gift to man. Freedom— sweet as a mother's caress. Like a pure white wing of a dove. Only those deprived of you truly know your worth!

In the centre of the platform is a sea of yellow and black: heads of hundreds of Jewish girls. Around them a cordon of black Gestapo caps and levelled guns. The girls wait for their specially reserved train to roll on to its tracks and take them in.

German women pass by the compressed mass of girls, glance at them as at a normal, every-day phenomenon. And walk on.

Fräuleins, teen-age couples, brown-uniformed Hitler Youth stroll by, cast a glance—and go on with their chit-chat.

Passing children unwrap the sweets their mothers bought for them, without looking up. All pass by, as if the Jewgirls surrounded by levelled machine guns were a normal, commonplace occurrence: part of the natural order of things; something which no longer draws the attention, having long since lost its attraction.

They stroll by the compressed clump of girls. They swerve around them as though they were a pile of luggage heaped in the centre of the station before train time. When the train pulls in, the porters will load it on. It's a freight shipment. What is there to see? They're used to the sight: always the same terror stark in the eyes. Always the same dumb faces. Sometimes faces of women, sometimes faces of men; sometimes faces of children, sometimes faces of elders. They've seen it hundreds of times. They regard it the way ushers regard a film which has been showing at their theatre for many months.

Trains come, trains go. Traffic is heavy. Germans.

Germans. Germans. The world is thick with their speech. Strident, angular, imperious, sends the flesh crawling. They converged here from all corners of Germany. Every one of them—a demi-god. Every one of them—a ruler of the world.

The same sky. The same trains. The world goes on its way. But Jewish girls, like bales of cargo piled along freight wharves, wait to be loaded up.

VI

The coaches were jammed with girls. They sat on the coach seats and on the floor. The train sped along. The doors and windows were sealed. *Wheels away to victory!* Daniella bent forward from her corner and looked toward the window. A verdant world sprawled outside. For a brief moment everything melted to a dense green haze. Nothing remained— neither Germans, nor Aktion, nor ghetto. Reality blurred, faded into endless green fields sweeping off to the horizon. Far off, a sun-congested sky bent over the earth like a mother offering the bare fullness of her breast to the mouth of her suckling. The train sped rhythmically along.

. . . She is sitting in a train car. She is riding. Around her, girls' heads. The same train. She is continuing the excursion with her classmates. Like a solitary thread of a cobweb wafting on the air, the thought streamed from her mind, wafted and spanned like a gossamer silver bridge from that train to this. Over this bridge her fantasy now roamed back and forth. And how sweet was this roaming, how precious the illusion . . .

Now she knows beforehand what will happen a moment later. Everything around her now has already happened before. A segment of another life, familiar in every detail. It was exactly the same way that other time. This is the way she sat in the corner of the car, and this is how it looked outside. A girl sitting beside her then asked the same question: "Is there any water on the train?" "Have to find out," was the answer then, too. The same tone of voice. The same colour train walls. The same green fields in the car window. Any moment and the farm cottages will come into sight. Here are the cypresses—

Daniella shakes herself up. The vision fades. The haze clears, vanishes. The silver bridge thins into a lone cobweb

114

in the air. She sees the slender thread; now it evaporates, vanishes into nothingness. Air.

Delusion.

The train rolls on. That time, the class mistress, Miss Helen, was standing at one window of the car, and the history teacher Viernik at another window. They were commenting to the girls crowding behind them on the sights beyond the window. In Yablova station the train suddenly halted. It wasn't moving on. Mr. Viernik barged angrily out to the platform to find out the reason for the delay. All the passengers went out to the platform. Then Viernik told the girls of his class to get off, too. The train stood empty with wide-open doors. From a distance it looked like the shell of a cracked nut—hollow, discarded. No lines available. The train cannot continue. The girls looked wistfully to the train. How soon will they be able to board it again and go on their way? Maybe this is the same train? . . . The train is continuing its journey. Nothing has happened. The train is continuing on the excursion to Cracow. How good it is now to dandle this illusion, to drink down its poison like intoxicating essence.

Farm cottages are scattered throughout the fields. Nothing has changed outside. Green fields. The sun still mirroring in the small cottage windows. The red-white mosaic of the shingled sloping roofs announces in bold numerals the years the cottages were built. In each cottage lives a family. An essay could be written about each family which would certainly win her first prize at commencement. That's what she was thinking then, she remembers.

Beyond the pane of the sealed coach door looms the head of an armed SS man, steel helmet lowered to his eyes, gun barrel swaying by his head. He stands outside on the platform of the speeding train and watches over the girls of his class.

Cottages.

Farm cottages. It was already night when she was fleeing Yablova market-place. The Germans had herded all the Jews of the town into the market-place. The first-term girls scattered in all directions and lost track of each other. Miss Helen didn't stop shouting: "Girls, keep together! Remember, together!" Until she didn't hear her voice any more. The voice was lost somewhere in the frantic mob, together with Miss Helen. The water jets from the fountain in the centre

of the market-place spurted skyward. The setting sun red-
dened the water and it looked like jets of blood spurting
heavenward from Yablova market. Then the sun went down.
The sky shaded itself with a strip of black night so it could
afterwards claim it had not seen what took place in Yablova
market. Where did she get the strength to run after all that?
How long was she lying motionless among the shot? She ran.
She didn't remember how she ran or how long. She ran. The
woods suddenly sprouted at her feet. If not for the knapsack, and if not for the bronze plaque on the diary in the
knapsack, she wouldn't be going to the labour camp now.
The diary is on the tile stove at the Centre. She won't be
needing it any more. What use will it be now? Everything
is excess. It's all over. She won't be any more. No one will
be any more. Maybe someone some day will find her diary.

More and more farm cottages. Oh, those cottages! Why
couldn't they have let her in at one of them? She would have
worked their fields. She would have worked hard until the
end of the war. She ran from Yablova woods for help.
Reesha Meyerchik, the star pupil of the class, was lying on
the ground pleading with her eyes: Help me! Help me! The
blood poured from her coat sleeve. She ran to the cottages
for help. The Polish farmer barked at her: "A Yid? Go on,
get out!" How she'd have worked for them. She got down
on her knees before them. Kissed the hands of the little Pole,
begged her to ask her father, her mother, to pity her and
not cast her out. She's also a schoolgirl just like her, just
like her. The little Polack wiped the wetness of the tears
from her hands, glanced sideways at her brother and let out
a shy, suppressed giggle. She was ashamed at having her
hands kissed. It's the first time in her life she's ever been
begged for mercy. She tittered and queasily wiped the tears
and kisses like slime off her hands.

Outside, in the cottage window, over a burning lamp, hung
an icon of the Holy Mother.

Now the sun mirrors in the same cottage windows. The
fields stretch green, boundless. The train rolls on. Where?
Girls on the seats and on the floor. Heads downcast, eyes
averted, as though it were shameful, this riding on the train.
As though it were they who were to blame for their being
led away thus now.

. . . These aren't the heads of the first-term girls. They
were shot in Yablova market. That time she thought she had

116

got away. Now again she's being led off. Again with girls. Where? Maybe to another Yablova market place. This time the train doesn't stop midway. *Wheels away to victory!* Her hand touches Fella's arm, as though wanting to cuddle up to her and tell her: "Let's always stick together."

Fella stares straight ahead, muttering as to herself, "They gulled me into the Dulag. Like a mouse into a trap. Now I know why they told me to go home a few nights ago. I let them catch me like a dumb dodo. Why didn't I see it? Back at the militia they told me to relax, nothing they can do now. I should go to the Dulag and they'll get me out. Abramek Glantz himself said so. Even got his dander up: 'What, Fella? Send you away? Such a thought! Why, you're one of the boys. Didn't I sign your card myself?' And how they gulled me into the Dulag."

Daniella can't stand the sadness on Fella's face. She's never seen her this way. She's completely changed—the way the sky looks to someone falling asleep by daylight and waking up to find it's night. Not the old Fella at all. In the ghetto Fella was used to being one of the *élite*. At the militia, where she spent her nights, she had come to feel she belonged to the safe and secure family. Like the militiamen, who were sure they would always be sending others to death, but not a hair on their heads would be touched. Now she feels sturdier than Fella. As though they had switched characters here on the train. Now she'd like to cheer up Fella, comfort her. But she doesn't. As though it would be an insult to the old Fella. The blow had hit her unawares. Now, on the train, Daniella feels as though the fear had become paralysed inside her together with the pain. Maybe because the word "labour camp" hovered day and night over her head like the death sentence over the head of a condemned; or maybe because deep down "labour camp" meant "Harry." Though the feeling was not completely clear, for how can it be that just in the place where they are taking her she'll find Harry and be able to be together with him? Even so the feeling did not stop surging through her subconscious, like a current under thick ice. This she knew: The current empties into a sea, the sea is called "labour camp," and somewhere in that sea is Harry.

All other thoughts and feelings swept along like bits of driftage on this powerful current.

Fella's face is cast over with despair. She has never seen

117

Fella this way. It hurts. As though all the agony of the Aktion were now concentrated in Fella's face. Daniella looks at her. She would like to tell her with the eyes what she can't bring out in words. She wants Fella to see her glance, understand it. But Fella keeps staring straight ahead, muttering as to herself: "Like a mouse into a trap . . . gulled . . ."

All the girls here were doomed all along, anyway. No one will last in the ghetto. No "special card" in the world is going to save them. All the girls here were earmarked for it. Some sooner, some later. A cracked plate in the breaking doesn't grieve the heart so; the breaking was expected. But Fella, she wasn't among the doomed. Fella blundered into it unawares. In her you plainly see a live, sound human being led to the gallows.

And that is a pity. That hurts.

A black uniform-shoulder shows at the door pane. Black. Black. Only the little swastika on the side of the helmet is red. A blood-spot.

That other time, it was Miss Helen standing by the window, expounding on the happy morrow of mankind—the Age of Television. Now the black shadow of the SS man stands there. At each and every window stands one of them. They are now conducting the "school excursion." His frightening eyes stare inside, scanning the girls' faces. By his face sways the perforated barrel of his machine-gun, and it looks as though the two of them—he and the gun—have taken the place of the class mistress, to pick up where she left off expounding the true meaning and essence of Modern Civilization.

VII

A vast terrain—sterile and unkempt. Behind her the German voices were still shrilling: "Out! Out!" She could feel the gun stocks pummelling the heads there as the train was being cleared: Out! Out!

She was afraid to look back.

From horizon to horizon ranged the ochre terrain, spattered with black stubs of dead bonfires; huge boulders wrenched from the bowels of the earth; overturned tree stumps with parched roots reaching skyward like gnarled, jaundiced giant-arms. The waste streamed like an immense river. Only in the distance stretched a dark range of trees, as though they had sprung back from here in fright.

The guns were levelled at them, fingers wrapped around the triggers. Six abreast, six abreast, the girls marched up the sloping terrain. Behind them the locomotive whistled. The train is heading back. *Wheels away to victory!*

There was not a trace of human settlement here. The only sign of a world—the railway lines reaching in—also came to a dead stop here.

Who pulled these stumps up by the roots? Who wrenched these huge boulders from the earth? It seemed as though vagrant spirits were busy at work here. Their presence was sensed though they were invisible.

Ranks of girls marched along. Precisely six abreast. Each vigilant not to step out of line or lag behind an iota. The gun barrels were fixed on them like the pupils of German eyes. The soil was sandy, loose. The feet sank into it. Some of the girls lost their shoes but didn't even try to retrieve them, as if they knew for certain they would have no more use for them.

A path cut through the trees. It was all hush, shadow, terror. The captives forgot where they came from. Forgot that once past, there had been years when they lived.

A gate. Overhead, German Gothic characters across the centre of an arc-shaped sign: WOMEN'S CAMP. Alongside, a postscript chalked in German hand: LABOUR VIA JOY.

10

THE gate slammed shut behind them. The ranks halted. Ahead lay a large square, and far off, beyond the square, a wooden bridge spanned a brook hugging the camp like a scimitar. The camp ground was inlaid with stones. Immaculate cleanliness. Rose-tinted barracks perched along bypaths amid beds of crimson blossoms. Gay curtains, lacework style, hung behind the barrack windows. An enchanted colour idyll. A suddenly unveiled wondrous corner of paradise.

To the right—chaotic wilderness. Exactly like the place where the train pulled up. Dingy, dilapidated shacks, like temporary shanties put up by road workers to shelter them and their tools from rain. It is obvious that there the camp is still in the process of building. In due time it will look there the way it does here.

A sanguine sun descended slowly towards the brook. The skyline blazed with red tongues of sunset. On the wooden bridge a black-uniformed sentry stood immobile, gun fixed on his shoulder. The sun flamed around his shoulders, and it appeared as though a fiery Gestapoman were on guard between sky and earth.

Near her the girls were whispering:

"Did you see the sign? *Labour Via Joy!*" . . .

"Work doesn't scare me. I'm not afraid of work." . . .

"Here, at least, we won't have to be afraid of being deported. At least we've got that behind us." . . .

"I'm glad I'm here at last. Just so long as I'm out of that ghetto hell." . . .

"Of course it's clean here. The Germans love it clean." . . .

"In the ghetto they think that in the German camps they kill people. See the sign outside? Maybe the work here is easier than in the ghetto." . . .

"Pity we can't be here together with our families." . . .

Harry! If she could only find Harry here . . . Maybe she'll run into him. As soon as she knows her way around, she'll start making inquiries. Maybe they'll even be able to work together. A camp like this would be an ideal place to wait out the war. The war won't last for ever.

Nearby, on the benches beside the gate, sit the Gestapo-men—the guards and escorts in charge of the transport. Now their faces look different. More human. Not as frightening as before. They sit on the benches all worn out, like porters taking a rest after carrying heavy furniture to an upper storey, wiping the sweat from their brows and waiting for a receipt that the furniture arrived safely. Some of them sit with crossed legs, the black Gestapo caps with death's-head badges on their knees. Their bared heads now look like heads of people. They are tired, and their tiredness gives off a latent human spark. Their fatigue unites them with the girls of the transport and creates a sort of kinship between the two groups.

Seems the ghetto people sent here are all alive, thought Daniella.

The German transport guards took off.

Heavy knells of a gong suddenly shattered the air, rolling like giant tin vats across the camp. Doors tore open. The Block-Curfew imposed on the camp because of the incoming transport was now lifted. The drowsing pink blocks came alive in a panic. The pandemonium recalled a sudden onslaught of Germans during an Aktion in the ghetto.

Out of the block gates charged bludgeon-carrying women, armbands on their sleeves inscribed KALEFACTRESS, hair cropped short, blue-pinstriped smocks, boots on their legs. On the faces of them all was blatant the same unspoken murderousness.

"Up! Up! Fall in!"

Far off, the gong boomed with an outlandish clamour.—The same clangs! When had she seen all this before? When had she already found herself standing here? With every knell of the gong, the livid twilight reaching from the skyline to the square resembled more and more the shaft of moonlight which had that time, during the clanging of the night tram, streamed in through the window of her children's-room. She felt her knees crumpling under her. She felt as though all around her time had come to a standstill.

"Fall in! Snap to! Snap to!"

They are being pushed, prodded along with bludgeons. Daniella runs with the others. A labyrinth of blocks. A queer new world. A world all blocks. Alleys and blocks. The enchanted paradise corner has long since vanished like a mirage. The kalefactresses goad the laggards: "Run! Run! On the double!"

The camp suddenly stood forth enormously vast and terrifying. Alleys and blocks. Blocks and alleys.

All at once the first true picture of Camp Labour Via Joy came to light.

Heads of skeletons, piled on top of each other, stared through the barred windows of an isolated block. The block seemed to be filled to the rafters with skeleton heads. Many of them shook bony fists at the newcomers being goaded past the block. Others rasped hoarse curses through gaping rows

121

of teeth. The flesh crawled: are these people or corpses? What is happening here? What kind of camp is this? Where are we being pushed? What do they intend to do with us here? Why are the skeletons shaking clenched fists at us? Why are they cursing us? ...

Like all previous newcomers, the girls of this transport too did not know that, because of their arrival, tomorrow, at the crack of dawn, a huge van will pull in to fetch these skeletons to the crematorium. How are newcomers to know that the veterans, the already-sucked-dry, regard them as their executioners? And how are they to know that it won't be long before they themselves will also be glaring out of the Isolation Block at new transports which will keep following them in here? And the newcomers will then look upon them as they now look upon these skeleton heads staring at them through the iron bars.

"Step it up! Double-time!"

Night began to settle on the camp.

III

Clerks, with white SERVICE PLATOON armbands on their sleeves, were sitting at a long table entering on cards the vital statistics of each new arrival. The girls of the new transport were led into the huge Service Block by fifties. Far back in the block, at a separate table, sat the camp doctor, a red cross blazoning from her armband, and beside her, at the same table, stood a woman: masculine face, steel-cold and silent, arms folded across her chest, a thick braided knout dangling at her side from one of the folded arms. She was wearing a brown, snug, turtle-neck sweater tucked into riding breeches, tall, polished boots, a black satin armband on her sleeve embroidered with scarlet silk letters: MASTER-KALEFACTRESS.

The Master-Kalefactress was silent, but her silence dinned into the deepest recesses of the immense Service Block. It was plain that here stood the suzeraine of the camp. Her eyes, the thin line of her clamped lips, struck fear into even the clerks of the Service Platoon. No wonder, then, that the dread gripped the new arrivals even before they knew what was going on here in the camp and before they had a chance to hear the voice of the Master-Kalefactress.

122

At the block gate, the groups pass each other: to the left —the exiters, putting on the camp uniforms issued to them from a pile, and to the right—the incomers, undressing, throwing their clothes on to the growing pile of dresses and coats, and, naked, going up to the long table where the preliminary camp formalities are performed.

The walls are lined with bludgeon-bearing kalefactresses. They stand erect, rigid, mute, their eyes commanding. A raw, slashing murderousness glares out of these eyes.

The exiters shamefacedly evade the eyes of the incomers, look down at the sabots they have just put on their feet. The wooden shoes clatter eerily on the floor. The foot doesn't lift, not daring to ruffle the awesome stillness of the Service Block.

. . . The shoes! The shoes they made at the shoe shop! She had made them herself . . . And here's the clothes heap! The very same clothes heap. Now they'll be using her coat to make shoes for others. It's all one world. A German world.

The camp smock gives off a queer smell. The smock is worn and frayed. Who knows how many girls this smock has already accompanied to the Isolation Block, from where the stripped body was delivered to the crematorium and the smock taken back to the Service Block once more to drape the body of a new arrival?

She stood naked. The locket! Where'll she hide the locket? She whisked it off her neck and held it fast in her clenched fist.

At the other end of the block, the last girls of the group ahead are going out. Their civilian clothes remain on the heap of garments, near Daniella. Where is she going to hide the locket?

The line moved forward. Girls of the new batch are already standing at the table. Stillness. Terrifying eyes of kalefactresses lower at the stragglers still lingering by the clothes heap. What's she going to do with the locket? Fella is already at the table. Daniella quickly moved up behind her.

The locket remained clenched in her fist.

Clerks were entering on cards, neatly and precisely, the vital statistics of each and every girl.

"Ever been sick?"

"What disease?"

"Anyone sick in the family?"

"Married?"

"Single?"

"Sexual relations?"

The line moved up. At a separate table, one of the clerks tattooed a blue serial number between the breasts of each approaching girl, and another immediately pressed into the flesh above the serial number a long electric stamp.

Because life was suspended before the eyes like an extraneous thing, the body did not feel the pain as strange hands jabbed a serial number into it, or as an electric stamp seared into the flesh the German inscription FELD-HURE. Neither the body nor the spirit felt any kind of pain that time in the Service Block of Camp Labour Via Joy.

At the last table, where the camp doctor and the Master-Kalefactress were waiting, the fate of each girl was sealed. There the die was cast as to which of the two sections of the camp she would be sent—Labour Division, or Joy Division.

Daniella halted at the last table. The doctor tapped her long yellow pencil slowly on the roster sheet and did not take her eyes off Daniella's lissom body. She suddenly stopped at Daniella's hand.

"Born with a closed fist, were you?" the doctor asked.

It flashed on Daniella's mind: in the ghetto, during the Aktions, anyone with a deformity was doomed to death. She quickly shifted the locket into the other hand and showed: here, she's not a cripple! She can open her hand!

The Master-Kalefactress, silent, arms folded across her chest, one booted foot thrust forward, all at once broke her silence.

"How's that? Let's have a look!"

"Pictures—pictures of my family."

The clamped, dark lips twisted toward the scarred cheek. It was a queer grimace—disgust, hate, perhaps a smile of a sort. Motionless, pose unchanged, eyes downturned—as if the arrivals from the outside world were not worthy of her glance —she hissed through sparse, stubby teeth:

"Get rid of that shit!"

The words drilled in her ears, splashing into ever-widening circles of echo. The twisted face of the almighty camp suzeraine bulked larger and larger before her eyes. The words of the command hammered relentlessly at her brain until she no longer knew what they meant. She whimpered, "The only remembrance. The only—"

The twisted lips turned towards the doctor and snapped, "Labour Division!"

The two words fell like a death sentence on the head of a condemned. The doctor looked waveringly at Daniella's lovely body and could not decide. But she at once got hold of herself: the Master-Kalefactress's command was waiting. The doctor looked at the number tattooed between Daniella's breasts, and began writing on one of the two sheets lying before her on the table.

The doctor was still writing the number as the Master-Kalefactress drew out the knout-holding hand until now folded across her chest. Placidly, coolly, she arched the hand way back, and with the same smirk on her austere lips brought the knout savagely down on Daniella's naked body.

"Tomorrow you'll throw the shit away yourself!"

The heads of the girls standing at the long table began whirling before Daniella's eyes. She ran to the exit. There they were issuing the camp uniforms. Between her breasts flamed the imprint of the electric brand, but she didn't feel it. Diagonally across her back—above the shoulder and down to the right side of her belly—a black welt shot up wide as the Master-Kalefactress's knout. Remnant fire sparks lingered in her eyes. She felt the flesh of her back constrict, as though it were clamped between the spirals of a steel spring contracting and pulling it back.

Outside, an indifferent night sky looked down at the camp. Somewhere a star twinkled like a firefly in the dark. The camp looked outlandishly vast, as if the whole world were contained within its confines. Far off somewhere, the wind played with the cries of women prisoners, bandied them about on the dark of night as in a game of ball. Red lamps lit a mesh of barbed-wire walls, which stood like a border barrier between one land and another. Far beyond the barbed wire, shadows of women prisoners moved to and fro under the amber light of a lantern like inhabitants of a neighbouring land—near by, yet foreign and remote.

Beside the wall of an adjacent block, Fella stood waiting for the girls coming out. Suddenly she noticed Daniella and hurried to meet her. They fell into each other's arms. Tears streamed from Daniella's eyes.

Her first tears in Camp Labour Via Joy.

IV

The block was huge and stark. Only all along the walls, a yard or so from the ground, iron rings were screwed in as in a stable. Hundreds of girls lay here on the floor of the Temporary Assembly Block—the transit block for new arrivals. From here the girls went in fifties to the nearby Service Block to complete the initial camp formalities. The girls of each returning group wedge themselves back in among those lying, slip mutely to the ground, and their silence merges with the silence already here.

Fear segregated the girls here and secluded each with her own thoughts. Although it was one and the same fear for all of them, it chose to deal with them individually. The girls lay on the ground as though they had not a thing in common; as if not the same fate had brought them together here.

Daniella sat leaning with the edge of her shoulder against the wall. The welt smarted on her back and wouldn't let her lie down. Near her two girls were weeping throttled sobs into each other, as though it were a disgrace to weep in this place. Fella lay silent, eyes fixed on the ground. A girl turned towards Daniella, her jet hair cascading to the ground. An exquisitely carved olive face, ebony eyes radiating youthful vigour—a true Semitic type. The undersize striped camp smock was unbuttoned in front, and between full breasts was the German inscription branded into her flesh.

"The last batch just left," she said.

Daniella didn't take her eyes off the inscription. She couldn't make it out.

"Maybe they'll give us supper now," the girl continued. "Haven't had a bite all day."

. . . What sort of mark can this be? FELD-HURE—what's the meaning of this strange German word? Across the brow of Shlamek's father they branded JUDE. There, blood gave from the seared word. And the word was as clear as the blood oozing from it. As though it were quite natural that the word JUDE should give blood. But this brand on everyone's bosom—its letters don't give blood and its meaning is obscure. What kind of word is this they've all been marked with?

126

Actually, they're all used to being marked—from the ghetto. It's no novelty. Though, the first time, it hurt when the Germans ordered all Jews to wear the shame-band on their left arms. All faces burned with mortification. At first, many stayed off the streets so as not to be seen with the shame-band. After a little while they grew used to it. A few days later Jews were back on the ghetto streets, going about their business again. Ghetto life went back to its old pace and no one cared any more—or seemed to remember—that there was a shame-band on the left sleeve. On the contrary: parents and children were quick to remind each other that they shouldn't dare forget to put on the mark of shame before leaving the house. In orderly homes a placard hung on the front door-knob: "Have you forgotten your shame-band?" It was a kind of new mezuzah which mothers and fathers made sure to fix on the door-posts. In homes where they still took pains with cleanliness, mothers would use the last bit of soap to wash the shame-bands thoroughly so the children would have immaculate shame-bands when they went outdoors on the Sabbath. Ghetto brides gave their grooms silk shame-bands as wedding gifts, which they embroidered in silk, with the German word JUDE inside a Star of David. The ghetto wind was always flapping with washed shame-bands hung out to dry. Then the new order came out: the Jew-mark will be sewn over the heart! Not the arm, but the heart. At first this, too, hurt. But you soon grew used to it, much more quickly than before. In fact, many were happy about this change, for the Jew-mark sewn on the clothing freed you of the constant fear of forgetting and leaving the house unmarked. When you got down to it, all the girls here were used to being marked. But this new mark—FELD-HURE—what does *it* mean? What connection does it have with the labour camp to which the Judenrat has sent them?

The girl noticed Daniella's eyes staring at her bare bosom. She said, with a knowing tone, "They've stamped us."

"What does this mark mean?" another asked.

"It means," the dark-eyed girl explained, "that from now on we're the property of the German government. My parents were horse dealers before the war. Two days before the war broke out, Polish government officials came to us and stamped the horses: 'Confiscated for the government.' We weren't allowed to use them any more. Same as now. They've stamped us to show that we belong to the German government. From now on no one is allowed to touch us. We'll work for the Germans, and in exchange they'll feed us. From now on, till the end of the war, we're the property of the German government. Anyway, we'll have somebody looking after us. Not like in the ghetto where we were public property, and anyone who could handle a smattering of German could do as he liked with us."

Fella perks her head up, looks at the girl clarifying the matter of the brand. It's obvious she has something to say, but she lets her head drop back to the ground. Her heart foretells her something altogether different. Fragments of conversation, bits of hints she had heard from militiamen now come back to her, and they fall into a pattern of sentences with an entirely different meaning. They told her back in the Dulag: "This is a super-strict transport, which has nothing at all to do with labour camp."

She didn't pay any attention to the words, then. Her mind wasn't on the transport but on ways and means of getting out of the Aktion altogether. A lot of things she hadn't put any stock in at all were just becoming clear. Only now are they really beginning to add up: the best-looking and healthiest ghetto girls were picked for this transport; Monyek, the Judenrat topkick himself, made up the list and even managed the Aktion. Fella knows that up to now Monyek never ran a labour-camp Aktion. They were always carried out by his militia stooges. The militiamen turned in as many heads as they were supposed to, but whom they brought— that was their business. Of course, for the Germans it was the Labour Commissioner running the show and he ordered them not to touch the girls at the shops. But this time it was all Gestapo. . . . Not a Labour Commission man in sight for this one. Fella knows who's who, and any kid in the ghetto will tell you that labour camp, that's strictly Labour Commission. So how did the Gestapo get in on this one? And how was it this time they took girls working in the Labour Commissioner's "war-essential" shops, when there are so many shirkers hiding themselves out in the ghetto? And on top of that, how was it they didn't let off a single one of the girls? Even the rich ones and privileged characters are here. Since when have money and pull stopped working with the Judenrat?

"The last batch is coming back," the girl said.

128

Opposite, on the ground, lie the Chebin sisters, the two Orthodox girls Hanna and Tzivia. They lie in each other's arms, each wanting to cushion her sister's head with her hand to make it softer for her on the hard ground. They look like two abandoned, terrified waifs. All the girls here are abandoned, but they seem to be the most abandoned of all. Hanna sits up, gazes about her with frightened eyes, and Tzivia's eyes follow with the look of a frightened gazelle. The camp smocks are too small and won't button in front. On their bosoms is tattooed the German inscription FELD-HURE. They don't know what it means, but their lips beseech, "God in heaven! Don't desert us!"

The block gate burst open. The girls sprang up as if by command. The Master-Kalefactress and her livery walked in. The letters on her black armband blazed red. It was enough to see the trepidation of her cut-throats in the presence of their boss for ordinary flesh and blood to freeze with fear.

The command rasps, "Number tattooed on the body will be studied and learned by heart!"

A Service Platoon kalefactress calls out numbers from a list. The girls whose numbers are called are stood to the side.

Five digits to a number. Hard to read them off one's own breast with fear running riot in the eyes. Frantically each asked the other to look at her bared breast and tell her exactly what the number was.

That moment they all became numbers, and ears pricked to hear if they were calling out the new designation they had been assigned a split second ago.

Daniella's number was FELD-HURE A13653, and Fella's number FELD-HURE A13652.

Joy has a thousand faces. And, so long as the blood flows warm within us, it does not forsake us. Now, as Daniella and Fella looked at each other's numbers, joy flashed between them: they're going to be together! Their numbers are together!

When Fella's number was called, Daniella was ready to follow her. But instead, another number, further up in the series, was called out. She had been skipped. Another girl stepped forward and moved into the called-out group.

"Labour Division!"

The twisted smile of the Master-Kalefactress floated up before her eyes. Labour Division! What does this word have in store for her? She didn't know whether it meant good or

129

evil. And it was the not knowing that frightened her so. Just as in the ghetto—the perpetual separation into two groups that splits the soul of the ghetto person in two; the never knowing which group is scheduled to live and which to die. That one group was headed for death—of that there was never any doubt.

The prettiest girls were called out to the separate group.

At the block entrance looms the cold, silent, boyish-cropped head of the Master-Kalefactress. *"Tomorrow you'll throw the shit away yourself!"* If at least Fella had stayed with her! Her eyes screwed up in pain. *The shit.* Her hand crept up to her bosom. A mark is branded on her body. She's stamped. Tremulously her hand touched the locket hanging there. She draws it out. In her half-open palm Moni's big velvet eyes look up to her:

"Dani, why did you leave me?"

"To bring you a present, my pet."

Her eyes fogged, as though clouds were banking on their rims. A grief she had never before felt engulfed her. Heavy tears dropped to the half-open palm. The tear haze overhung her eyes and blurred them. The white bows on her braids in the picture lift and settle over Moni's velvet eyes. And in her mind, as in the photograph, the words overlap each other:

"Tomorrow you'll throw the . . ."

"Dani, why did you . . ."

The two large groups were lined up. The called-out numbers were marched to the left section of the camp—the Joy Division, and the others to the right side—the Labour Division.

V

29—

An electric lamp barely lit the number above the block gate: 29. The number of the block to which she was assigned. Daniella pushed the gate and entered.

She froze to the spot.

A blurred, endless road hung over with fog. Countless human shadows, streaming to and fro through the fog, not knowing where to or where from, without pause, without rest. Everything as under murky water. Overhead, in the cavities between the rafters, flickering lamps, showing everything here to be yellow, beyond solace. The other end of the barrack is invisible. An unending road. On both sides, along the walls, two layers of boards, one above the other. Above and below, countless human shadows draped in tatters, lying and sitting, wedged up against each other. Rags on the feet, rags on the heads. No telling their sex or age. Skeletons. Skeletons beyond count. Wherever the eye reaches—skeletons eddying along in a stream of yellow murk.

The gate tore open. A bludgeon-bearing kalefactress appeared in the doorway, and roared, "Up on the boards!"

Daniella ran to the boards and tried to climb up. From above, mouths bared enormous teeth at her, eyes dilated with hate, and feet kicked and stamped at her hands, not letting her go up. A newcomer! Her face gives her away! Below, the kalefactress was batting the heads of the stragglers still scurrying around on the block ground. The blows echoed like the drubbing of clubs on empty pots. Daniella scampered frantically back and forth until she finally managed to wedge up on the boards among others.

The boards were spread with filthy straw as in a slimy cowshed. The others drew back from her in hatred, avoided her, as though she had come here of her own will to usurp their place. Just now they are very busy. They have no time for her now. Each has a rusty can standing between her legs. In the can is the muddied tea ration. They are waiting feverishly to get their bread ration. They have no time for her now. She, the newcomer, must think she's going to outlive them just because she got here after them. But just let her wait. Tomorrow, at the Baustelle, they'll teach her a thing or two.

The gate opens again. Two kalefactresses. One shrieks, "Shut up!"

Two prisoners carry a basket full of even portions of black bread. The bludgeon-armed kalefactresses follow. Row upon row of prisoners sit shoulder to shoulder on the straw. One of the kalefactresses following the basket tosses the bread at the prisoners. Prisoner after prisoner snatches at the meagre black crust, which must do until the next day at the same time.

Daniella automatically grabs for her crust and holds it in her hands. Though she hasn't had a bite since the day before, she doesn't feel or even remember the taste of hunger. In

131

fact, even were she being forced to eat, she wouldn't be able to swallow.

Her neighbour clutches the crust with two fleshless hands. With flaming eyes she examines the crust from all sides. The rusty tea can stands between her thighs. She throws open a mouth full of enormous, poised teeth. It looks as though the teeth would swallow the crust down in one bolt. But the teeth just embrace the bread, touch it and let it out whole. The teeth grind and grind and the crust remains in the hands the same as before. Perhaps the bread has dwindled a bit, but the decrease is not noticeable from one bite to the next. The teeth bite into the bread again and again, embrace it with ecstatic fervour, and once more release it—whole. Yet the black crust in the hands grows smaller, smaller, until nothing is left of it. But the teeth don't let up baring themselves and biting voraciously into the grimy, fleshless palms where earlier there had been a piece of bread. When she tired of lapping at the memory of the bread, her eyes shifted towards the portion still lying untouched in Daniella's hands. The eyes sank into the black patch of bread and sucked and swallowed it from afar.

Daniella looked dazedly about her. She was still bewildered. This all can't be real! Can't be! . . . Just then she felt cringing, beseeching eyes riveted on her. Instead of the lashing hatred of before, there now looked from the eyes the wistfulness of a forlorn, sick old woman. Their glances met. The woman wearily lowered her head and didn't let out so much as a sigh.

At the sight of this look, the block and everything in it faded. Daniella's heart twinged. She suddenly wanted very much to embrace the old woman's head, crush it to her heart and burst into tears.

The woman laid her head on the straw, bent towards Daniella. She didn't take her eyes off the bread in the newcomer's hands. Daniella suddenly understood. She quickly held out the bread with both hands to the beseeching eyes.

"Eat, dear heart," she said.

The old woman slowly lifted her head from the straw, looked from the bread to the head of the newcomer, and back again to the bread. Seeing the hands still outstretched towards her with the bread, she snatched it with her nails in one swoop like a beast of prey, clasped it behind her—

and waited. Now she was ready to kill and be killed if that one should dare to take it from her.

The gruesomeness of hunger now stared at Daniella out of two bottomless eyes.

She repeated gently, "Eat, dear heart. I really want you to have it."

The old woman avidly sank enormous teeth in the bread. She was still incredulous. She looked at Daniella and gulped. Looked and gulped. Then she brought the tin can to her lips. Suddenly she jerked the can away, stopped chewing, covered her emaciated face with gnarled hands and broke into a choked sobbing. A left-over of the nibbled crust remained lying on the straw by her knees.

Daniella reached out her arms to her and embraced her. The old woman lay on her bosom like the frail body of a sick child. Gradually her weeping subsided. She lifted her eyes and looked up at the tears streaming soundlessly on Daniella's face.

Daniella gently caressed the bony, jaundiced face. She picked up the left-over lying on the straw and put it in her mouth as one feeds a spoonful of medicine to a sick baby.

All around, on the boards, the prisoners were already in the throes of sleep. The old woman asked feebly:

"Where did they bring you from?"

"Jew-Quarter 3," Daniella answered.

"And I'm from Jew-Quarter 1," she said. "Still any Jews there?"

"There are still Jews working in the shops."

"My name is Zeidner. Renya Zeidner. During the first round-up they separated me from my family. I was sent here. I'm the only one left from my transport. Maybe those there, on the other side, those at Doll House—maybe some of them are still around. Would you happen to know if any of my family were saved from the round-up? We lived at 19 Slovatzky Street."

Daniella knew of no such family. She herself hadn't been in the Jew-Quarters when the first round-up took place, and except Harry she didn't know anyone in Jew-Quarter 1. *Doll House!* What does that mean? What sort of camp is this?

"I'm really from Kongressia," she answered. "Because of the war I got stuck in Metropoli. I don't know anybody in the Jew-Quarters. What do they do in this camp? What sort

133

of shops do they have here? What's over there, on the other side?"

No sooner did Renya Zeidner hear the mention of "the other side" than her eyes flared up with hate.

"Those there gorge themselves on our bread! Sausage, margarine, two portions of soup a day. All the tea they want. At the 'Public Chastisement' you'll see how stuffed they are. From our camp they take Mussulmanesses out to the Isolation Block every day, but they, they have a 'chastisement' only when a new transport gets in. It's all the same to me now. I won't be suffering here much longer. But before I die, I'd only like to know if any of my family are still alive. How I wish I could see at least one of them before I'm packed off to the crematorium."

The old woman sank back on the straw, exhausted. Her eyes gazed somewhere far, far away. Daniella couldn't get another word out of her about the camp. The old woman had left her completely for her own world of the past. Perhaps home, perhaps her children. An indescribable grief now lay on the bony face. Daniella felt guilty, as though her being here had brought it about. Her appearance from the outside world must have reopened forgotten wounds in this poor wretch's heart. And to distract her from her pain, she asked by way of conversation:

"Mrs. Zeidner, how old are you?"

The old woman wearily turned her eyes to her. Without changing her position on the straw, still sunk in her reverie, she answered:

"When the war broke out, I was in first term high school."

Daniella's limbs froze. She wanted to get up to run, to scream. To run and scream. But she was like one caught in a horror dream who wants to escape but cannot: the limbs won't obey.

From among the rafters two lamps blinked dimly down like the surly eyes of a monster crouching overhead to guard the prisoners. On the boards lay hundreds of women's bodies. They looked like rank, mildewy rags spread out beside each other to dry. They were asleep. Their breathing was inaudible.

Renya Zeidner, the girl not yet graduated from high school, closed her eyes, slipped off to sleep. From her gaping mouth protruded her upper teeth, jutting directly out of the fleshless gum bone.

Daniella shielded her head with both hands, as though to ward off the horror swooping on her—
She is the same age as this old woman ...

VI

"Up! Up! Up!"

After three such roars from the kalefactress, pandemonium breaks out amid the straw. Everyone scuttles quickly down the boards, as if they were not a moment ago floundering in delirious sleep, but had been waiting tensely all night long to hear the commanding roar "Up!" like field runners poised to take off at the starting signal.

Renya Zeidner shook Daniella awake to spare her the kalefactress's bludgeon. It took a while before Daniella came to, before she found her bearings. Now she was more exhausted and weaker than the others.

Outside it was still dark. At the block gate they were passing out tea, a leafy swill. All the women stood in line, holding their rusty cans. Throughout the day they wore the cans on their hips, from a string or wire girding their buttonless smocks, and at tea distribution or noon-time soup they took the cans off their hips.

Renya came back from the tea barrel. She found Daniella and offered her the can of tea. Although this was the second day that Daniella hadn't had a bite or a sip, the mere sight of the can nauseated her.

Outside, a new day was making ready to enter the camp. At six o'clock work begins. The tools have to be prepared. When Hentschel, the German overseer, makes his daily inspection, each girl must be able to show that her tool is ship-shape. Woe to anyone with whose tool Hentschel finds fault.

Masses of prisoners were dispersed over the Baustelle. The other section of the camp, with its red flowers and rose-tinted barracks, was not visible from here. As if it didn't exist at all. Here there were pits, mounds, and rocky soil. Solitary rail carts stood on temporary tracks. No one knew or asked what, actually, was being built here. Thousands of budding lives had this earth already devoured without one of the victims knowing toward what end. For by the time a miserable strip of earth was levelled out, a whole transport of

135

girls had perished. And the newcomers did not know what their predecessors had produced here, nor would they live to see what their successors would accomplish.

All hurry to put their tools into trim. Their bodies swarm with lice and grime, but Hentschel the Moon, the German overseer, takes great pains, before work starts, to see that in the handle joint of the shovel there isn't—oh dear no!—a speck of dust.

On the square Daniella suddenly caught sight of Hanna, the elder of the two Chebin sisters. Hanna threw herself into Daniella's arms with an outburst of tears. Hanna—who in the ghetto had borne her misery uncomplainingly, without tears, accepting everything lovingly, as God's punishment— now sobbed helplessly like a child. They'd taken her sister away from her! Last night they separated them, and Hanna is afraid that little Tzivia will be lost without her. About everything around them here on the compound, Hanna doesn't say a word: her first night in her block, where she lay among living dead, she doesn't even mention. She cries only about her young sister Tzivia: why did they break them up? How will Tzivia ever manage without her?

Daniella looks silently at Hanna. Isn't it just the way she felt when she heard that Harry was gone? And last night when they separated her from Fella? But where is all this going to get Hanna?

"Let's always stick together, Hanna," she said.

She took Hanna by the arm, and as they went told her how she had met this old-timer. There she is now, polishing her shovel.

They both went over to Renya Zeidner.

Renya now looks much younger and more alive than last night on the straw. She is sitting on the ground, scraping her shovel blade with a stone. Renya is genial towards them, unlike the other prisoners who regard the newcomers with open hostility. For always, with the arrival of a new transport a Selektion[1] takes place. The huge van comes up to the Baustelle. Hentschel the Moon takes girls away from work, orders them to put their shovels aside, and climb on to the van:

"Into the blue, *mein Liebchen*. They're buildin' them a highway there!"

---

[1] Selektion: the weeding out of weaklings to be sent to the crematorium.

Such are Hentschel the Moon's little witticisms as his workers, whom he has already sucked dry of their marrow, climb into the van which is to take them to the crematorium. The vacated spot is immediately filled by newcomers, and the shovels pass into new hands. Everything is back to normal, until a new transport arrives, and newcomers again take the same shovels and move into the places of their predecessors. Thus the shovels pass down from hand to hand, uninterruptedly, and thus, uninterruptedly, the veterans look upon the newcomers as their death warrant.

Renya Zeidner stretches out in the yellow sand. She has finished scraping the shovel, and is resting a bit. The shovel lies on top of her, its gleaming blade on /her bosom. She holds the shovel in fast embrace, as a lover.

Renya Zeidner is in good humour. Today work will probably start two hours late, and that gives her a holiday feeling. Today she can take it easy at a time when, on any other day, she'd already be hard at work. Today the inferno is sure to start two hours later: they brought a new transport to the Joy Division last night, and they're bound to have a Public Chastisement this morning. Otherwise, Hentschel the Moon would already be on the Baustelle. If that's the case, Renya can let herself loll a while in the sand. It's holiday in the camp.

"Those there," Renya points to the Joy Division, "pack in a good bellyful before they get to the oven. True, they end up climbing into the van just like us, but while they're alive they don't starve their guts out. It's with our bread, our drops of marmalade that they fatten them there! And the beating they get on their last day? We get it plus every day!"

VII

Three heavy knells of the gong carried across the camp. The sky deflected their echo over to the Baustelle. Kalefactresses stormed out of barracks, bludgeons like flags in their hands, batting the prisoners' heads towards the Execution Square. All prisoners, of both sections of the camp, have to attend Public Chastisements in the Joy Division. When a flogging is put on, all the prisoners are required to watch the spectacle.

The German way, you know.

137

The two sections are partitioned off by a double wall of barbed wire. In the centre, between the walls, is the Execution Square.

Joy-kalefactresses lead some twenty girls, nude, into the square. Each one is strapped over a separate stool—the feet to the forelegs of the stool, arms to the hindlegs, face down. Beside each stool a kalefactress stands by, bludgeon ready. The Master-Kalefactress silently directs the Chastisement. All eyes are fixed upon her for the starting signal, but she, in turn, is waiting for Yaga, the blonde Camp Commander, to make her appearance with her entourage to watch the Sin Purgation about to be performed.

When the "Blonde Beast" shows up, the Master-Kalefactress cracks her knout down on the back of one of the kalefactresses—the starting signal, and they, specially trained for this murderous task, get to work.

Bludgeons rise in one cadence, with Germanic measure and precision, and swing down in unison on the naked bodies. Without pause, without letup. The shrieks split the heavens, geyser from the stools out of key, off rhythm, but the lofty heavens obediently keep their silence, as by German command.

Strung on the barbed wire along both sides of the Execution Square—eyes. Eyes beyond count. Prisoners' eyes, witnessing from both sides of the camp the pageant of Sin Purgation now being presented on the Execution Square.

The black van stands by. Kalefactresses hurl in the mangled bodies of the "purgated." The van then swings around toward the Labour Division, in passing, to pick up the skeletons at the Isolation Block.

In the Labour Division, the Mussulmanesses crawl of their own accord into the van, appearing like a death crawl of corpses returning voluntarily from the night, one after the other, into their common burial pit.

VIII

Hentschel the Moon, the German overseer, really has a head like a full moon; rotund, ball-shaped, as if traced out with a compass, clean-shaven, tiny ears, a wisp of a nose, a slit of a mouth—all topped with a mass of pink flesh, and a thick, heavy cudgel set in his hand.

When Hentschel flogs—and Hentschel flogs to death—it is never discernible on his moon face whether he is doing it out of annoyance, or hatred, or for the sadistic fun of it. He is like a machine brought here to kill, and kill he does with exemplary precision.

It may very well be that at home Hentschel has a wife and children; it is possible that he is careful to go to church every Sunday; perhaps in the circle of his family, relatives, friends, Hentschel is known as a meek, modest person; is first to say "hello" to everyone, gets up for a lady on the tramcar. It may be that until war broke out Hentschel was employed as a competent, reliable clerk in a construction company, and every morning, at exactly the same time, his wife prepared him a ham sandwich for lunch; and every morning, at exactly the same time, he gave her a good-bye peck on the brow before leaving for work. But here, in Camp Labour Via Joy, Hentschel swims day in, day out, in a sea of blood, in an inferno of human misery for which no language in the world has the idiom.

With the very hands with which, at exactly ten o'clock every morning, Hentschel takes the Butterbrot from its neat wrapping—obviously prepared by dutiful wifely hands—with those very hands he daily crushes young, quivering girlish lives.

It may very well be that after such a day, Hentschel returns home as he used to from the office: takes a footbath; neighbours drop in for a chat or a game of dominoes; a canary warbles in the cage hanging from the lintel of the open window; in the yard, children play basketball. Hentschel gets up, pours water into the flower pots on the window sill: flowers are like people. They are alive. And just as people must have food, flowers must have water. Deprive them of their water—they wither. And that's very sad. Hentschel feels how sad.

It may even be that with his own hands Hentschel fills the saucer with milk and sets it on the floor for the kitten he is raising at home.

Later, when the neighbours leave, Hentschel takes the bulky watch from his vest pocket, winds it for the next twenty-four hours, and makes ready for bed. Tomorrow, first thing, he has to get up again for work at Camp Labour Via Joy.

IX

The girls of the new transport have no work tools. The van has already taken off. Because of the Purgation, Hentschel was late in coming to camp today and didn't have time to make his Selektion. Therefore, there aren't enough tools to go around. So Hentschel assembles the newcomers, studies their faces, sizes each one up individually, and with his expert connoisseur's eye estimates: who'll hold out at work, and who'll up and fizz out?

"Damn fish-nation!" is Hentschel's routine curse. "Like fish out of water: some last a while and some rot on the spot. . . ."

Hentschel has a foolproof method all his own. He knows that first and foremost he has to teach the newcomers what he means by work. He knows that the only source of strength for work in this place is fear. The main thing—fear! Therefore, it's up to him to reveal this source to them—immediately. That's the way he always does it. He's tried and he knows.

On the ground lie temporary rails, over which rock-filled rail-carts are pushed from place to place. These rails always have to be carried from one place to the other. Just the thing for breaking in new transportees.

Hentschel gives an order. A batch of new transportees go in between the rails, and line up in file along the whole length of them. The rails are bolted to thick wooden ties which are imbedded deep in the earth because of the constant pressure of the rock-filled carts. Hentschel's head is all nonchalance, like the moon disk. Come to think of it, there is a crinkle of a smile on his face, the like of which only children see on the face of the moon.

When all is set, the Moon lets out a screech: "Get hold!"

The girls bend down, "get hold" with their hands, right and left, of the cold iron of the rails. The Moon again screeches: "Lift high!"

The girls are stooped over, fingers clamped on the rails. The rails don't budge. The weight of the iron itself is beyond their strength, let alone when it is bolted to ties, and not to mention when the ties are rooted in the earth and the earth is recalcitrant, holding the ties fast between clenched teeth and stubbornly refusing to let go of them.

Each girl is absorbed in herself, bowed to the earth as in mute prayer: Please, merciful earth, please let the rails go.

At first they didn't notice. But the screams shocked them into awareness. They cocked their eyes and saw: Hentschel stands over Hanna of Chebin, and pummels her body unflaggingly with a shovel handle. As though he were drubbing unctuously, with sacred purpose. As though the very drubbing were the purpose.

Hanna is sprawled over the rails and Hentschel bastes her feet, her head, her arm-bones. Hanna screams to God, writhes on the ground, bites her teeth into the sand, tears at her hair. Her teeth strain out of her mouth, her eyes tear from their sockets, and the Moon stands over her—placid, unruffled, not the least bit angry, and with no effort at all goes on laying the thick handle into the shoulder bones, at the ankles, the wrists—beating, beating. Hanna wants to die. She wants to die:

"God in heaven!!! Take me! God in heaven!!! Take me! . . . God!!!"

But Hentschel doesn't let her die.

Hentschel is now in pitched battle with "God in heaven." He won't turn Hanna over to God so quickly. Hentschel is as stubborn as the recalcitrant earth, which refuses obstinately to let go the rails. Hentschel knows that Hanna has to come across with many more hefty screams before she dies. All the new transportees must afterwards go on hearing the screams for as long as they are assigned to his jurisdiction. And he lays into Hanna's bones calculatedly, methodically. Just so she doesn't pass out. Because once Hanna stops screaming —she'll be dead. Oh, he knows this from experience. It never fails.

"Get hold!" Hentschel's command shrills a second time.

The girls pounce upon the rails, sink their fingers into the iron.

"Lift high!"

The source is revealed. Fear generates superhuman strength in the hands. Hanna lies on the ground. Something still stirs within her. A foot, a hand, something lets off an occasional twitch. A twitch, and then no more. She lies still, a hollow

141

husk. But the echoes of her screams still hover aloft, grate on the air.

Now the battle is joined between the earth and delicate girlish hands. The battle for the tie-bolted rails. It seems the girlish hands are stronger than the might of the earth, for bit by bit the ties slip out of the clamped teeth of the earth.

Hentschel screeches: "Spine out!"

That is: backs straight, posture proud and erect while carrying the iron rails. The earth draws the rails back with an indescribable magnetism. The earth hasn't given up yet, it seems. It wants to retrieve its own. But on high, above the erect heads, Hanna's screams flurry about as though hurled back unanswered from the heavens:

"*God in heaven! . . .*" "*God in heaven! . . .*"

And girlish hands overcome the magnetic might of the earth. They carry the rails.

The girls vanquished the earth in the battle for the rails, and God vanquished Hentschel in the battle for Hanna's soul. Kalefactresses fling Hanna's corpse into the Isolation Block so it shouldn't get in the way on the Baustelle.

Hentschel takes the bulky watch from his vest pocket: exactly ten o'clock. He seats himself on an overturned cart to have his lunch. He peels the neat wrapping off the Butterbrot, and daintily sinks his red lips into the sandwich. As he munches, his tiny eyes rove all over the Baustelle, like a contented rancher surveying the bounty of cattle grazing in his pasture. A current of nervous diligence galvanizes the hundreds of girls bent over their work:

"Chick! Chick! Moon's watching."

X

Parade.

All the newcomers are lined up on the square, naked. Yaga, the Blonde Beast, and the German chief physician behind her are coming to inspect the new transport.

The chief physician passed slowly before the girls, closely examining each one. Reaching Daniella, he paused, looked at the black edges of welt on her left shoulder and right side of her belly—a souvenir of the Master-Kalefactress's knout. He knit his brows: What's this? Flogging here, in the German labour camp? He was flabbergasted, as though a

142

flagrant breach of German ethics had been committed here. He pointed with his finger to the shoulder. "When did it happen?"

Daniella remembered the locket hidden among her rags on the ground. She kept still.

The chief physician scanned her body and couldn't figure it out. There must be some mistake. Undoubtedly, a mistake. He ordered her to open her mouth, peered into her eyes, fingered her breasts, and finally turned to the Camp Commander and discussed something with her in whispers.

Yaga went up to Daniella, also examined her closely, and asked, Had she any internal disease? Had she ever had a contagious disease? Was she married? The very questions the clerks had asked two days ago in the Service Block.

"No," Daniella answered to question after question.

The Camp Commander ordered Daniella to step out and dress, and stood her to the side. When parade was over, and the new transportees had gone back to Hentschel, Yaga took Daniella along to headquarters. There she looked up Daniella's medical card, and had the Slovakian doctor summoned to her—the same doctor who had entered Daniella on the Labour List.

When she entered the office, Yaga welcomed her, first of all, with a kick in the belly, and only then pointed to Daniella, growling angrily, "Such a flower you send to the quarry? You've got too much of this brand in your whore house?"

As of that moment, Daniella belonged to the Joy Division.

11

THAT day, Harry left Tedek's three potatoes intact; didn't touch them, didn't even go near them. However, Tedek never got to eat them.

Through the barred lattice of the sick bay Harry heard the prisoners singing: "Gals I Adore . . ."—a sign that they are already marching in from the Baustelle. Of the songs they are made to sing on the way, this is the last one as they approach the camp gate. As a matter of fact, there is something hopeful and promising about this ditty, both in the lyric and in the tune. Every prisoner feels it. For while the mouths are singing about "Gretel's tall tits," the eyes already see the ladle of soup they'll soon be getting in camp, and the limbs feel the bunk boards where they'll soon be able to lie down. Since the SS men first noticed that the prisoners sing this ditty with more gusto—that is, no need to crack any skulls with the gun stock so the others will be convinced that while marching to and from the Baustelle there must be singing—and since they think it's the contents of the ditty that causes it, they always order "Gals I Adore" to be sung on approaching the camp gate. Let the Camp Commander hear how lustily his prisoners sing.

Harry goes out to the parade ground. Soon roll call will start, when the Camp Commander will get the report: So-and-so-many dead, so-and-so-many alive. All must be present and accounted for.

The first ranks march into the camp, line up on the parade ground according to regulation: the short in front, the taller to the rear. Their mouths are still singing the last bars of "Gals I Adore" as the last ranks march in through the gate with the dead on their shoulders, lay the corpses' heads square with the feet of the first rank, one alongside the other, legs stretched out straight, hands folded on the belly cavity —can't have anyone out of line. Now, it isn't improper for a long one to lie beside a short one. Just so long as the heads are in an even line with the feet of those standing in the first rank.

Harry stands at the other end, a few steps away from the ranks, as befits the dignity of his white smock with the red cross emblazoned on the sleeve. His eyes search among the rows: Where can Tedek be? Why doesn't he see him?

"The Cat" comes out of the German Quarters. Already without his gun. He suddenly remembers something, calls the Jew-Chief over, hands him a slip of paper scribbled with two names of prisoners whom he orders him to punish with all due severity.

"Twenty in the arse! Get that, Spitz" the Cat snarls with his toothless mouth at the Jew-Chief.

The Cat is an old SS man, completely toothless, with two drooping, scraggly whiskers fringing his puckered mouth; hence his nickname, the Cat. He sits dozing in the Baustelle sun all day long. But as he starts up between naps and wants to convince the skies above, the world around, his comrades, and the conscience within him that he really hadn't been asleep at the switch, he whips out his black memo book, calls one of the prisoners over and takes down his name and number. Later, in camp, he remembers, rips the page from his memo book and hands it to the Jew-Chief, so that he should make a good example of those he bagged at the Baustelle. The Cat is too old and lazy to carry out the punishment himself. But never mind. Leave it to Spitz. Not a single prisoner has ever got up from the wooden bench after Spitz has counted "twenty in the arse" into him.

And let everyone get this: The Cat does not snooze.

. . . Where on earth is Tedek? Every time Harry glances over the rows, he collides with architect Weisblum's cadging look which proclaims: "Here I am, right here." He wants Harry to see him, not to forget about him. The collar of the architect's jacket is disjointed and frazzled. The jacket is mouldy and coming apart at the seams. Through the rents shows a bare, grimy shoulder bone. His shaved skull is spattered with sun-baked muck and mud from the Baustelle. "Prince of Wales," Sanya used to call him in her gay moments. And he took great pride in his nickname. She liked him for his stylishness, and especially for having lifted himself by his own bootstraps to his high, secure position in life. The most modern buildings of Greater Metropoli were built according to architect Weisblum's designs. Even Metropoli's anti-Semitic city council had to call on him to design new municipal structures. Twice a year he went abroad to acquaint himself at first hand with the latest developments in modern architecture, and he never forgot— be it in New York or in Paris—to send Sanya his snapshots; and he never failed, as soon as he was back from a trip, to make an appearance before Sanya in the elegant foreign suits he had picked up on the trip. *"Prince of Wales."* And the title really fitted him. His splendid manly figure was just right for his dashing clothes, which always became the rage. The "Weisblum ties," "Weisblum shoes," "Weisblum angle" of the hat brim—these all set the vogue for the Metropoli play-boys. Men discussed his clothes with the same admiration that an original Biedermeier is talked about. He was the darling of the Metropoli snob set, and was accustomed to being pampered by the cooings and coquetries of sleek socialites. Yet, he would always pop up in the Zakopane snow mountains whenever Sanya went up there for her favourite sport, skiing, even though no one told him about it. He would always know, somehow.

145

Seems he was really in love with Sanya.

Now he stands here, this "Prince of Wales," in the roll-call ranks, fixing a beseeching sidelong glance on Harry: for the sake of their common feelings for Sanya, would Harry please remember to give him a few spoons of his soup?

"Prisoners! At my command, atten-tion!"

Roll call is on.

The prisoners stiffen up, not breathing, not stirring, as dead—all, of course, except the really dead, who go on lying on the ground placid, indifferent, hands folded over their belly cavities, no longer concerned with roll call. They are free men and they flaunt it publicly. They don't as much as bat an eyelash at the "Attention!" but go on gazing at the sky spread over them like a white quilt, and dream their free, tranquil death dream.

Except for some whose faces are contorted as if in nightmare. Perhaps it is the German labour camp that has now intruded upon their dreams, warping the tranquillity on their faces.

The Jew-Chief runs up to the Sturmbannführer, salutes and reports. The Sturmbannführer wheels around to the Camp Commander, salutes and reports. The Camp Commander strides along the first rank, counts the feet. Where the feet end the skulls begin, and he counts them in the same breath.

The number checks. Everything is in order. Roll call is over. The prisoners start running and jostling into the block, line up for the soup distribution. Each wants to get there first. Hunger will not take second place on the soup line.

Harry does not move. The prisoners stream past him like water flowing around an impeding stone. He scans, looks intently around for Tedek. He wants to bring him into the sick bay. The architect is carried along by the stream. As he catches sight of Harry, he looks back as though meaning to halt, but he can't make up his mind: to keep running, or linger a while so Harry should see him. He looks back at Harry as though he has something urgent to tell him. Finally, he lets himself be swept along towards the block. Apparently, he cannot give up the chance of being among the first in the soup line.

The parade ground empties. Something horrible begins to dawn on Harry, but he will have none of it. He feels the mere thought unsettling his knees. A noisy racket issues from the block. Standing here, outside, you hear the tumult louder than inside. There, to the jangle and clatter of tin plates, the prisoners scuffle into line as though after gulping down the watery soup their hunger won't be a thousand times worse. There, in the block, life still makes a row. But here, across the parade ground, death lies in hushed repose. Soon, all those now clamouring in the block will also be still as these laid out here head beside head—silent, silent.

Hadn't these arrayed here on the ground fluttered and clamoured this very morning at bread time just like those now brawling in the block?

The parade ground is empty. Dread thumps in the heart. He is afraid to cross the square. He wants to hold the illusion a little while longer: maybe Tedek is in the block. Maybe he missed him as he ran into the block. In the mind the truth is clearly established, but he still refuses to face it. The parade ground is empty, and the sky, too, is empty. Harry's eyes strain at the corpses laid out beside each other by the wall there. Inside the block the prisoners are already jostling toward the soup barrels, while these, on the fringe of the square, continue to lie rigid, fixed, as though unaware that roll call is over; as though they had turned to stone during roll call and now have to be wakened: why don't you get up? Soup's on!

On the other side of the barbed wire, an SS man comes out of the German Quarters, without the black jacket, without cap, just in his white undershirt. He saunters down toward the washroom carrying a white towel and soap. The wooden clogs on his feet clippity-clop on the stone path, recalling the idyll of a labourer returning from work in the evening and going to freshen up with a cold rinse. He is whistling "Gals I Adore," and the tune sounds queer coming from the mouth of an SS man, as though the song were part and parcel of the prisoners, an inseparable element of their lives. As though the words "Gretel's tall tits" sound right only coming out of prisoners' mouths and only they ought to sing them.

The parade ground is empty. Harry walks over to the other side. He doesn't even feel his legs steering him to the wall; doesn't even wonder why he's heading there now. Simple. He's the medic, and it's his job to go to the wall and examine the dead.

The first—is Tedek.

His jacket is askew, exposing his mangled body. The

trousers are shredded, as though the cloth had burst under the thrashing he had taken, and his mouth is twisted as though poised to bite at someone. He looks directly into Harry's eyes. He's still alive! His pulse isn't beating any more but he's still alive! You can plainly hear him. A scream struggles within him. The twisted mouth doesn't stir, but the scream seems to erupt through the open wound holes on his body. The eyes are alive. They're screaming to him. Beseeching him to help.

Tedek! Tedek! ...

Block orderlies come out of the block. They've already picked up their soup, and now they have to carry the corpses into the Carrion Shed. They start dragging them.

"Damn these stinkin' carcasses! Man can't even eat his soup in peace!" one of the orderlies hisses through clenched teeth, snatches angrily at one of the bodies and starts dragging it by a foot.

"Doc! They're dishin' out the soup in the block," another says servilely as he takes hold of Tedek's foot.

Harry bent over. "Let me," he said, and took Tedek in his arms. The dead man was light as a desiccated skeleton. He carried him in his arms to the Carrion Shed. Above his arms the sky lay over the dead man like a white sheet. The SS man sauntered back from the washroom, towel slung over his arm as he ran a small comb through the damp hair on the back of his head, carefreely whistling and with his wooden clogs beating out the rhythm of "Gals I Adore."

"Seems Doc's got time on his hands," one of the block orderlies whispered to the other. They hurled the corpses one after another into the Carrion Shed and hurried back to the block for any soup scrapings left on the bottom of the barrel—which were traditionally the prerogative of the block orderlies.

He laid Tedek gently on the ground. The dead man looked back at him with live eyes. He had never seen Tedek with such live eyes here, in the camp. The borderline between life and death was all at once completely obliterated.

He suddenly felt like saying, "Tedek, I've put three boiled potatoes aside for you in your hutch. See that you eat them tomorrow morning before going to work, and take the bread along to the Baustelle."

He wanted to tell him, "Tedek, honest, you look better than ever today."

An indomitable will now looked out of Tedek's eyes—mettle, manliness, determination. You could see: *"The lad knows what he's after and he'll make it."* The same old Tedek! The same Tedek whom he, Harry, had sought in vain throughout their stay together in the camp. All Tedek's vanished qualities were now again glinting in his eyes, but in all the stark, silent ruthlessness that is appropriate in the Carrion Shed of Niederwalden.

In the corners of the shed heads of rats popped up, their round black eyes gleaming amazement. They were looking directly at Harry, trying to understand: Is Doc alive, or what? If he's alive—what the hell's he doing here in the shed? What's he butting in for? Do they stick their noses into his business in the sick bay? Na-a-a, they take their time. They know they have theirs coming to them here. The shed's their stake and the corpses are their stake. They're not doing so hot, either. Fat meal they're going to get here on the crummy scraps that hog of a Baustelle leaves them!

Tedek's body was mauled and mangled. The sore-holes showed through his tatters. The torn skin on his body was like ripped oilcloth of a toy horse which gives no blood. He bent over Tedek's head and with two outstretched fingers drew down his eyelids. Only now did Tedek lie dead. His warped mouth now seemed like a congealed scream, the last scream of a tortured Mussulman, whose pain is more horrible than the most horrible death.

There is no more Tedek. Never again will he be able to bring him into the sick bay. Tedek will never be leaving the camp. The last of his hopes now lay on the ground of the Carrion Shed. Only now did Harry feel the real horror of Tedek's death. Only now did he comprehend it. His hands clenched. *"Let's revolt as one man against the Germans,"* Ferber had pleaded. Sanya wouldn't hear of it. Not because Sanya was a coward, but because of her overwhelming determination that he, Harry, survive the war. And even he couldn't reconcile himself to the idea that after suffering so much in the ghetto, Sanya and Daniella should be killed by German bullets. Now he is here in the Niederwalden Carrion Shed. And what will happen to him after all the others have passed through this shed? What kind of death will the Germans concoct for him? Sanya works in a good shop, and Daniella in the Labour Commissioner's shoe shop. The feeling that Sanya and Daniella are outside fills him with exaltation, purifies his suffering as through a distillery of martyrdom. Like one whose neck is in the noose, and he knows he is about to die so the others may live. Did Tedek have anything to reproach himself for? Hadn't he sacrificed himself for others? *"I'm going out of the ghetto to bring life to others." "I'll pave the way for you."* Hadn't this tormented Mussulman done all he could, and more? *"I'll pave the way . . ."* Who knows, Tedek, what kind of way you are now again paving for us?

Through the planked door of the Carrion Shed heads of prisoners peer in. They are waiting around impatiently for the medic to leave the shed. They want to take the shoes and rags off the corpses, and they don't understand. Why's Doc hanging around the Carrion Shed today?

The rats have emerged completely from the corners. They stand motionless, looking and waiting: does he really mean to go on sticking around here till the van shows up to haul the carcasses off? All right, all right, so respect the dead. But enough's enough!

Outside, the day was ebbing over the parade ground. Harry started towards the block. In the distance stood the prisoners, all eyes. He looked up at them. They stood scattered around the parade ground, hanging on to his glance.

The same rats' eyes! The same stares. Rage and nausea swept over him.

"Hyenas! Disgusting hyenas!" he raged at them. "Let one of you so much as set foot in the shed!"

They fidgeted and shifted in embarrassment. They were taken aback: What's so special today? Why is he suddenly butting into none of his affair? One of them looked dumbly at the rags wrapped around his feet. He diffidently approached Harry, lifted pleading eyes, and barely stammered out in a feeble voice, "Where's the harm, Doc? I work barefooted on sharp rocks all day long. If I don't take their things the van will only get them anyway. Where's the harm, Doc?"

He turned away from them, didn't say a word, and continued towards the block. He could still see the contorted, pleading face of the prisoner. It occurred to him that Tedek had sturdy shoes on his feet. These shoes had been meant to cross the Beskidian woods and mountains on the way to the Czech border. Vevke must have put all his fatherly warmth into the making of these shoes; they held out so long.

150

"Where's the harm, Doc? If I don't take their things the van will only get them anyway. . . ."

He continued with lowered head toward the block.

II

Near the block entrance was Spitz's flogging bench. Beside the bench stood "Red" Itche-Meyer; behind him, his son. Spitz had one booted foot propped on the bench, his rod in one hand and the Cat's memo in the other. He eyed his victim—the fifty-year-old red-haired Itche-Meyer—fondling his rod as one who enjoys his craft, and waited for the second prisoner on the list to report to the bench. He took another look at the memo and shouted into the block:

"Zanvil Lubliner! Come and get it! Snap to! Twenty in the arse!"

Spitz was a stumpy fellow of about twenty, born in Germany. His sister worked at the Labour Commissioner's office in Metropoli, for which Spitz regarded himself as a man of high station. When he was sent to labour camp, she probably used her influence to get him appointed Jew-Chief. Actually, no one knew if he was born in Germany, or if he really came from Galicia. He himself boasted of having been deported here from the old Reich. He talked pure SS, had a large hump of a nose, arched like a sickle, which gave his face the appearance of a vulture.

Red Itche-Meyer stood ready. Spitz was looking at him, but he didn't return the look. They were both aware that after "twenty-in-the-arse" the flogged man would be carried off to the Carrion Shed. Red Itche-Meyer's shaved skull was violet. The flutter of the slender veins in his temples was visible even at a distance. Along his emaciated neck ran a bulging vein, like a water-filled hose. Behind him stood his son, swaying like a man in a prayer trance, ceaselessly pinching at the shrivelled skin of his hands.

Zanvil Lubliner emerged from among the wooden hutches. His glance stumbled over Harry's. He said nothing, immediately looked away from Harry as though ashamed, and continued towards the bench. Harry felt his blood freeze. He ran to the bench and let out a shout, "No! Zanvil is a good worker! I've got to bandage his wounds now. I won't let him be killed!"

151

Spitz took his booted foot off the bench, sheathed the rod in his other hand and again drew it out from the clenched fist as a sword from a scabbard. He parked himself arms akimbo, like Siegfried, the SS man, when he is about to lay into a prisoner.

"Zanvil! Down on that bench with you!" Spitz ordered.

"No! I say no!" Harry shouted firmly and resolutely. He inserted himself between Zanvil and the bench. His chilled blood now gushed full strength into his arteries. He felt his arm sinews tighten. Now he was ready for anything: "No! I say NO!"

"Medic, keep your nose out!" Spitz warned. He shoved the paper slip into Harry's face. "There, there's the Cat's memo! Who's got to answer for it anyway? You or me?" he yelled.

"Go to the Camp Commander! Make out a complaint. I'll take the punishment on myself! You hear? Myself!"

"I've got an order and I aim to carry it out. You go and complain to the Camp Commander. Tell him I'm killing a good worker. But better watch out, medic."

"Not worth it, Preleshnik, not worth it," Zanvil murmured from behind Harry.

"Down, you red carcass!" Spitz swung around to old Itche-Meyer. He was furious. It was clear this Jew wasn't going to get up from the bench. Harry felt that with his own hands he had galvanized the rod in Spitz's hands.

Just then Itche-Meyer's son sprang forward from behind his father. He dashed to the bench, flung himself upon it and cried, "Jew-Chief! Have pity! Flog me instead of papa! Dear Jew-Chief! Sweet Jew-Chief! Have pity, flog me!"

Red Itche-Meyer, who all the while had stood like a stone pillar, suddenly came to life. He leaped on to the bench and clawed at his son's throat as though meaning to strangle him.

"Away from here, Pini! Away from here! Be off with you!" Sparks flew from his eyes, and the bulging vein on his neck swelled to the point of bursting. "Away, Pini, Pini, away!" he screamed.

Harry suddenly remembered something. An idea flashed through his mind. He went up to the Jew-Chief and whispered into his ear. "Spitz, I have an 'R.6' back in the sick bay."

"Why didn't you say so in the first place? . . . Whoresons!

152

Back to the hutches with you! I'll fix you later!" he bawled with feigned anger at the two doomed Jews.

"R.6" was a privileged German cigarette, available only to Reichsdeutsche, which Harry had come by in a strange way.

That same day, as Harry sat in the sick bay engrossed in thought, the kitchen door was flung open and together with the ribald German voices someone burst into the dark block and staggered for the sick bay. Harry wanted to rush up into one of the hutches to hide, as he always did when the sounds of drunken revelry carried from the German Quarters. But this time he didn't quite make it. In the sick bay door he saw the dishevelled hair of the blonde German whom he had seen through the barred lattice a while ago. Now she was drunk, half nude, and her two full breasts protruded from her open blouse. She regarded him in weird rapture, fell at his feet, embraced them with her nude arms, and half in weeping, half in ecstasy, blubbered, "Oh Holy One, come with me . . ."

The Camp Commander came running in. He tore her off him, lifted her from the ground and led her back to the German Quarters. Along the whole length of the block she continued struggling to break back to the sick bay, and didn't stop blubbering:

"Oh Christ! . . . Oh Holy One! . . ."

After a while the Camp Commander returned to the sick bay and smiled as he said, "Well, Physician, you looked pretty scared of the blonde Magdalen."

He pulled out his cigarette case, lit himself a cigarette, and before the case was back in his pocket, there tumbled to the floor—a cigarette.

"Relax, Physician. You won't be bothered any more," he said.

This isn't the first time that such a cigarette "drops" from the Camp Commander's case in Harry's presence. It happens every time the Commander comes to inspect the sick bay and finds everything to his liking: bottles arrayed on the table with utmost precision, in even, symmetrical ranks, like soldiers. He especially likes the inventory lists tacked on the wall. He is fascinated by the sight of the neat handwriting and the perfectly straight lines drawn there. No remarks to make. Everything is just so. Upon which the Camp Commander takes the cigarette case from his pocket, lights himself a cigarette and down the floor comes rolling an "R.6."

For Harry such a cigarette is a real salvation. He has even devised an original technique of smoking it. He doesn't inhale the smoke but eats it. A whole week after getting the cigarette, while eating his bread crust, he takes a draw on the cigarette. The smoke blends with the chewed bread in his mouth and he swallows them down together, the smoke with the bread. And ever since he first started eating and ever since he first started smoking, he has never savoured such a delicacy. A true ambrosia. Such a combination of bread and smoke tarries longer in the stomach. The usual way, you don't feel you've swallowed anything. The bite passes through the mouth, down the gullet—and it's all over. As though it had vanished into thin air. And the hunger in the stomach and the guts is right back where it started. In fact, now it's more insolent than ever. The guts have heard a rumour that the mouth has eaten. So they come contracting and converging: hey, what's this we hear about the mouth eating? Well, where is that grub? What's coming off here? Who's trying to pull a fast one on us?

But when the crust in the mouth is saturated with a draught of cigarette smoke, then they all really feel the taste of food: the palate, the stomach, the intestines; and the mouth is titillated by an aching delight—the divine, sweet-toasted savour of the cigarette.

Now, with Spitz standing with the death rod over the lives of the listed two, and there was no way of saving them, Harry suddenly remembered the Camp Commander's gift—and his "R.6" cigarette saved two Jews from the Carrion Shed.

Zanvil Lubliner stood just behind Harry. When Harry turned around, he met his glance. Zanvil returned him a moist, tear-laden look. At first, when he came to the bench, his eyes were brittle as clay shards. And now suddenly they are running with tears. Zanvil looked, said nothing, and walked off to his hutch as the Jew-Chief had commanded.

As Harry made his way back to the sick bay, Pini bent over to him from his third-tier hutch, strained down toward him with outstretched head and arms, and sobbed, "Oh, Doc, Doc."

That was all he was able to let out.

Harry continued toward the sick bay. From the other

end of the aisle between the hutches, Spitz called across to him, "Ho, Doc! I'll be around to the sick bay after last gong!"

Harry didn't reply. He continued walking. Near the sick bay he heard his name called. He turned his head and saw architect Weisblum.

"Mr. Preleshnik, I thought I'd tell you that at the Baustelle today an SS man killed Tedek with a shovel. You think maybe from today on I could have the half-soup Tedek used to get from you?"

Harry felt the blood surge into his brain. He bit his lip, swung around, and went into the sick bay.

He turned on the light. Outside stood a long line of sick. They were waiting for the medic to save them.

12

IT wasn't until late in the day that Daniella felt the pain begin to let up. The savage fire which had been raging in her lower abdomen subsided somewhat. The scorching heat that had been burned through her vagina still fulgurated and lapped within her full strength. The focus of the pain—at first concentrated on one point where it drilled as with a white-hot drill—dulled somewhat as the pain spread throughout the body.

Large beads of sweat streaked down her naked body. She had only just become aware of them. Only now did she feel herself weltering in the pool of sweat streaming down her own body. She lay with upraised, splayed knees fastened to two vertical iron rods mounted on the table to which she was strapped. From time to time the lower part of her spine irradiated a lacerating pain, like a tongue of flame shooting from an already-smothered fire, and raced up into the teeth clenched in the mouth and down to the toe-nail tips of the dangling feet. Gradually the intervals between one pain stab and another lengthened. But the strapped life within her always anticipated the stab to come.

Through the wire screen of her cage she saw in the opposite cages girls embroidering red flowers on linen tablecloths. The block window was hung with a gaily coloured paper curtain. It was pinked lacework-fashion and its centre was cut out with figurettes and animals, just like the curtains she saw from the distance in the windows of the pink blocks the day she got into the camp.

Through a side door two medical orderlies in white smocks rolled in a table on small rubber wheels. A girl's hair cascaded over the edge of the table. The stillness in the block stood heavy and opaque as before. They brought the table up to one of the cages, opened the door, pushed the table in, went out and locked the cage door behind them.

Through the main block entrance the German chief physician followed by his staff of assistants trooped in. The chief physician's face was studious, like the face of a scientist engaged in important research. He was wearing a white, turtle-neck smock, but on his head was the black SS cap with the death's-head badge in front. He went from cage to cage, examining the notations on the black slates attached to the screen of each cage. His speech was sober, composed, his voice earnest, exactly the way it was when he saw on her body the mark of the Master-Kalefactress's knout—

Flogging here, in the German labour camp? . . .

He went from cage to cage, looking in at the girls, examining them from outside the screen, like a scientist observing his guinea-pigs. The girls didn't look up. They went on embroidering the flowers on the tablecloths.

In the rows of cages opposite were the girls whose experiments lasted for extended periods: artificial insemination, twin insemination, miscarriages, premature deliveries, and various methods of castration and sterilization. The row of cages on the left belonged to the Surgical Experiment Department. Here the girls were replaced very quickly; they didn't last long. Female organs were removed from their bodies and replaced with artificial ones. On them were tried all sorts of poison tablets, which German pharmaceutical concerns sent to the chief physician to be tested on humans. Naturally, the concerns paid handsomely for the experiments, at rates fixed by the chief physician.

Here was the camp's "Science Institute." The Institute was hidden in a side path among beds of crimson blossoms. Even the barbed wire here was bedecked with fragrant creepers. Admittance was strictly forbidden to outsiders.

INSTITUTE FOR HYGIENE AND SCIENTIFIC RESEARCH declared a small sign outside.

Whenever a new transport arrived at the Joy Division, the girls would go through the Surgery Block of the Science

156

Institute, which was emptied to receive them, and here they were all sterilized in one batch. By the next day, they were all ready to be admitted to the Joy Division. Since Daniella was an extraordinary case, she was sterilized in the Research Block, in a cage which happened to be available that day.

The chief physician came up to Daniella's cage followed closely by his assistants. Here he stopped and studied Daniella.

... Schultze! Schultze in his black Gestapo cap aiming the tip of his cane at her eyes! She's lying on the ground in the woods.... Another minute and Schultze will inflict a horrible death on her ...

Through the wire screen, the eyes of those standing outside looked in at her as into the cage of some rare creature in a zoo. She was lying naked, her parted knees still strapped to the iron rods at both sides of the table. In the hand of one of the assistants she saw the same instrument which they had that morning inserted deep into her vagina. Her body shuddered instinctively.

... The instrument reaches out to her eyes like Schultze's cane. Now they're going to bring Harry in. They'll hold him tight, make him watch what they do to her ... She wanted to scream, but, as in the dream, the screams stuck in her throat. Her strapped life writhed within her. Her whole body trembled.

The chief physician looked at her with benign eyes and said soothingly, "Now, now. Tomorrow you'll be out of here." And turning to leave, he finished the sentence towards the assistants: "The *Jungs*[1] will be pleased with her. . . ."

From the adjacent room the Slovakian doctor came in. She held a glass jar in her hand. Inside the jar a bloody chunk of flesh, shaped like a human heart, floated in clear liquid. She handed the jar to the chief physician. He held it up against the light of the window, examined the organ through the glass of the jar. He then went up to the cage where the girl who had been wheeled in was lying. He looked alternately at her and at the excised organ floating in the jar. Then, with white chalk, he drew over the whole surface of the black slate attached to her cage two lines forming an X— that is to say: Everything entered on the slate is hereby null and void. The Experiment-Unit will die. Tomorrow the cage is to be available.

[1] Jungs: boys.

The chief physician was grave. He pointed out Daniella's cage to the Slovakian Doctor. "The treatment has to be completed there," he said. "Tomorrow the cage must be vacant." He went out of the block, his assistants respectfully and deferentially at his heels.

The block was all silence, as if there were not a living person in it. Why hadn't she heard her own screams when the Slovakian doctor lit the fire inside her belly? She could clearly feel herself screaming—as though she had screamed into a deep vacuum.

No one here let out a sound. It was still as in an underground aquarium. The cages lined the whole length of the block walls, looking like cages with drowsy animals who had been brought in for the day into a temporary tent of a travelling circus. Now they are resting. At night they will be put on show to the crowds.

Nurses came in carrying trays, loaded with white and red bowls. They wore white linen shoes; their steps were inaudible. Silently they approached each cage, opened the door, set down a bowl of food, locked the door. So from cage to cage. By the notations on the black slate they knew where they should place which colour bowl, and with which cage they were not even to bother. In the X-marked cages they knew it was a waste to put any food. Better save the portions for the cages of the Experiment-Units with the pregnant bellies.

The creature in the isolated cage stares tensely through the screen. It can't wait for its bowl of food to be put in. The eyes stare dumb and imbecilic from under long, bushy eyebrows, and the mouth is mute. When it was installed in the cage, it was a lovely young girl in her bloom. Now it looks like a mummy unwrapped from its shrouds. The brow is pointed, the hair growth abnormal and its complexion bizarre. The face is ploughed with wrinkles, like the meat of a walnut. No indication on this creature whether it is male or female. It looks more like a man. Its behaviour is normal, like a denizen of this planet, which belongs, however, to some ancient, primeval era. As though the Germans had succeeded in resurrecting their Neanderthal Man.

The Slovakian doctor returns from a nearby room. She opens Daniella's cage. The treatment has to be completed. The cage must be available tomorrow. Her every movement tells how riled she is. Apparently, she still hasn't forgotten the kick in the belly she got from the Camp Commander because of Daniella. Angrily she jerks open the leather straps on Daniella's arms and upraised knees, pulls a blood-test syringe out of the breast pocket of her white tunic, jabs it irritably into Daniella's arm and snarls, "So it wasn't good enough for you in the Labour Division, eh? You just had to come here! Well, the soldiers here'll teach you!"

Inside the glass tube of the hypodermic needle rose the crimson liquid. *Her blood!* She looked at it. The sapped-out blood suddenly became terribly close. It seemed to her they were now extracting her most intimate, her final essence—her life! The innermost within her, which she herself has never seen, is now being transfused into the glass tube. They're going to turn her into a crimson creature! Queer red hair! A pointed brow! They will seal her in a glass jar and there she will float about for all eternity.

The doctor completed her treatment. She went out and slammed the cage shut behind her.

Daniella lies on the table unstrapped, but she feels herself unable to move a limb. *"The soldiers will teach you . . . the soldiers will teach you . . . the soldiers . . ."*

. . . A trolley jammed with girls . . . midnight . . . a yellow bulb burning overhead . . . the hanging straps swaying to and fro, to and fro . . . "13" presses a girl against his body and his hoarse Germanic voice jeers: "The soldiers will teach you." "If you knew where you're being taken, you wouldn't be struggling out of my arms now . . ."

Slowly she sat up on the table. From the opposite side the white X stared back at her from the black slate on the cage of the girl who had been wheeled in before. The head of the girl tossed and turned without cease from side to side, to and fro, to and fro, like the hanging straps on the trolley ceiling. Her eyelids were shut tight. From time to time her mouth twisted into a grimace of horrible nausea, or as though she were screaming in a horror dream. But not a sound issued from her throat. Daniella scrutinized her closely. The face looked so familiar. Where has she seen this face? She just couldn't place it.

In the opposite cages the girls with the pregnant bellies were embroidering red flowers on white tablecloths. They didn't raise their eyes from the linen. Their hands worked flick, flick, and suddenly halted, with the needle stuck in the linen. Again flick, flick, and again halt. As though their

159

thought had suddenly snagged. The block was still as an underground aquarium. Girl-hands—like little fish, darting flick, flick, and suddenly halt, absorbed.

. . . Of course! This is the girl who had lain next to her on the ground in the Assembly Block the night they got here! The same girl who had explained the meaning of the German word FELD-HURE on their flesh: "We'll be the property of the German government, the way my father's horses became the property of the Polish government. From now on we won't have to worry about a thing," she said. "The Germans will take care of us. They'll feed us and nobody will be allowed to harm us any more."

Now she lies there in the cage, and the organ which had vitalized her budding maidenhood like the lush seed of a fruit-bearing tree now floats in a transparent jar in the room of the German chief physician. Maybe he will succeed in transplanting this uprooted chunk of life into the belly of a German woman, and there the organ will go on living, bring its fruit to the world—many more German scientists like himself.

"*Till the end of the war we'll belong to the Germans . . .*" For this one lying there the war is over. The white X all over the black slate above her head certifies that. Her pain is gagged within her. The Research Block doctor has delimited it: it may go as far as her throat, but no further. She is silent, as all the others here are silent. In the Research Block it must be quiet. Absolutely quiet. So as not to disturb the research being conducted here for the benefit of civilization.

INSTITUTE FOR HYGIENE AND SCIENTIFIC RESEARCH.

Outside stretch lovely vistas of trees and blossoms. The block walls are steeped in roses. The roses are red, and from the distance the German Science Block seemed afloat on a blood lake.

13

JOY DIVISION.

Here, in the rose-tinted blocks, there was no flogging. Here they kept close watch over the girls' bodies to keep them whole, undamaged. Here, when a girl was flogged, she was not permitted to return to the Joy Division. She was immediately tossed on the van and—*off to the crematorium!*

Here every girl got a new outfit. Every week—clean underwear. Compared to the food in the Labour Division it really was paradise here, as Renya Zeidner had said. But the girls who lapsed into sin in this paradise received a "report." Just a "report." Sinners with three such "reports" were led out, usually with the arrival of a new transport, to the Execution Square, where Elsa, the Master-Kalefactress, cleansed the sin out of their bodies. Sin Purgation it was called. Upon which the purgated bodies were tossed on the van. Let the other maidens of paradise behold and beware of sin.

Here, every day, at two o'clock, German soldiers, on their way to the Russian front, came from the nearby transit depots to entertain themselves with the girls of the Doll House. The girls had to put their all into the satisfaction of their esteemed guests. If such a guest was not satisfied with the "enjoyment," he had only to report it, on leaving, in the orderly room and give the girl's breast number. After three such "reports" the girl was automatically doomed: she hadn't duly appreciated the great honour bestowed upon her; she had made light of the honour of a German warrior!

Elsa, the Master-Kalefactress, is a pure-blooded German from Düsseldorf. The green criminal-triangle patch on her brown sweater denotes that before the war she had been sentenced to life imprisonment. What crimes had earned her this penalty no one in the camp knows. What is known is that when the Germans established this camp, they took her from prison and brought her here to serve as Master-Kalefactress. And the choice turned out to be a happy one—the right person in the right vocation.

Elsa of Düsseldorf is now the almighty suzeraine over the dwellers of the Joy Division. The crude stitching of several knife slashes on her face makes it difficult to determine her age. She has a tall, slender frame, which she is constantly trying to emphasize by wearing tight-fitting riding breeches, which she tucks into her boots cavalry style. She has two narrow slits for eyes, clamped lips and a long, dark scar-ridden face that is constantly aflame with unsated sexual desire and violent jealousy. It may very well have been her monstrous outward appearance that had made her a leading candidate for this post.

It's possible that men had always shunned Elsa. Her lacerated face may even be a souvenir of that. But here, in the Joy Division, where she is almighty ruler, Elsa is consumed with jealousy of her subjects and gives them the brunt of it. During Enjoyment Duty she roams through the blocks, craving to draw the attention of the German guests. When they arrive in camp, she greets them in front of the blocks, struts her pure-German pedigree before them. She puts a black satin band on the other sleeve, too, for all to see from all sides just who and what she is in the Joy Division. But it's no use. Not one of the soldiers is receptive to her overtures. They spurn her and choose to go into the blocks to her despised serfs.

For such carryings on the almighty suzeraine has already taken a public flogging. She once set upon one of the guests and tried to bend him to her desire. The soldier extricated himself from her violent embrace, spat in her face, and went into the orderly room to complain. Out came Yaga, the blonde Commander, and with the braided knout in her hand let the panting Master-Kalefactress have it across the head. Elsa took the flaying in silence. Only her lips writhed madly and her eye-slits shot arrows of hate at the Blonde Beast. She knew that Yaga went every few days to her lover—the commander of the nearby labour camp in Neiderwalden—to cool her own lust. But she also knew that she must take the flogging in silence. For to Yaga, Elsa was just another prisoner. Later Elsa took out the lashing on the girls whose sole ruler she was.

During Enjoyment Duty Elsa roams through the blocks, ostensibly to see if the girls are applying themselves properly and giving their guests full satisfaction. She observes the girls as they lie under the soldiers, eager to catch them at the sin of "indifference." She reminds the guests that they may complain about it; that in camp headquarters such indifference calls for a "report."

Elsa wants to slake the fires of her lust with the blood of the girls. Indeed, the height of her pleasure is in purging the girls' bodies of sin in the Execution Square.

After Enjoyment hours, when the Germans have left the camp, Elsa stalks through the camp like a frenzied beast in heat. The girls all quake in terror. First the Germans, now Elsa. Out of one hell and into the next. Every so often Elsa gets hold of one of the girls, drags her into her room, throws herself upon her and sniffs all over her body, drinking into her nostrils the scent of the man who had just detached himself from the girl. Woe betide the girl who does not

162

fulfil all Elsa's desires. Elsa knows how to make such a girl reach a state where she will automatically get a "report." But who is the girl who can gratify the bottomless passion of Elsa of Düsseldorf?

There is no measuring Elsa's elation when it is given to her to announce to a girl that she has used up all her "reports." Her eyes heat up in glee. The girl stands hypnotized. Both Elsa and the girl sense that the victim now belongs completely to Elsa: both her body and her soul have now passed irrevocably into the title of the Master-Kalefactress. Elsa's mouth goes into weird contortions. Her thin lips bare tiny, sparse teeth. She fixes the girl with the eyes of a python about to entwine its prey, and with diabolic slowness rolls out the words:

"I'll purify you . . . Now you are mine . . . All mine . . . I'll purify you proper . . . But first, come with me . . ."

The girl stands transfixed. Elsa's eyes are inside her eyes. She can't wriggle free of the eyes. She does not scream. She does not weep. She does not flee. She stares at Elsa's face and sees in it the Execution Square. The picture of Sin Purgation is familiar to her in every detail. She has seen it more than once. Now she is numb. Elsa's arms wrap themselves around her. The hands paw her whole body, draw her up against the brown sweater. Words reach her ears from Elsa's twisted mouth as out of the depths of hell.

"I will purify you . . . Purify you . . . But first come with me into my room . . ."

Elsa of Düsseldorf walks, leading her victim pressed close against her body. Both take heavy steps, as in a trance. They pace toward the room as if going there to perform a ritual; as though here, in Elsa's chamber, were the sanctuary of the New Human Civilization.

II

When Daniella reached the square of the Joy Division, Tzivia of Chebin ran to her. She is anxious to know how her sister Hanna is getting along in the Labour Division, from where Daniella is now coming.

For a moment Daniella stood there dumbfounded. She was not prepared for such a question. The Research Block had made her forget completely the Labour Division. But hardly

had Tzivia sounded the name "Hanna" than the scene came
back to her as though it were just happening: Hanna slung
over the rails and Hentschel the Moon placidly circling her
body, and with the shovel handle laying, by turn, into her
elbows, her feet, her head—waiting for her to scream. Scream
all the more. But scream. The more harrowing, the more
heart-rending, the better Hentschel will like it. As though
Hanna's screams were music to his ears. Hanna's screams
again resounded in Daniella's ears as though Hanna were
now screaming here, right beside her:

"God in heaven! God in heaven! . . ."

Daniella stood there dumbfounded. Tzivia looked directly
at her mouth, waiting for a reply.

"What is it, Daniella? What's happened?" Tzivia asked,
frightened.

Daniella shook herself instinctively, like one coming to
after a stunning blow on the head. She remembered that
Tzivia had asked her a question and snapped:

"What do you mean 'how is Hanna getting along?'? She's
working, like all the others." She wondered why the words
came out of her mouth so crossly.

"I've heard they work very hard there. How does Hanna
feel during work? She's so weak!" Tzivia added, with great
concern.

By the outlet of the lake girls sit scrubbing their eating
utensils. On the bridge stands the SS sentry, gun propped on
the railing, barrel pointing at the girls. Red bulbs gleam on
the poles of the barbed-wire wall, indicating that the wires
are charged with high tension. To the right range the rosy
blocks; girls go in and out of them. Through the narrow
spaces, whiting between the blocks shows the barbed-wire
wall running on the other side of the Joy Division. From afar
it seems to have sprouted from the earth together with the
crimson flowers. Just beyond the barbed wire, the Labour
Division; the Baustelle. Renya Zeidner there is surely thinking of her now—so she's gone over to the Doll House! Now
she'll also be getting two soups every day, gorge herself on
the sausage and margarine which by rights belong to the
Labour Division girls! And when they lead her off naked
to the Execution Square, her eyes will bump into Renya
Zeidner's eyes through the double barbed-wire mesh. Renya
will then see how stuffed she is. Renya will look. No! Just
don't let her look at her that way! Renya's eyes pierce her

164

through and through. She can't bear that look. She's being led naked to the stools in the Execution Square and Renya's eyes look with scorn and loathing—

"How does Hanna feel there during work?" Tzivia repeated, her eyes still on her.

Daniella wants to avert this horrible conversation. She feels she just can't bear it. The wire fences and the block roofs swim before her eyes. Another minute and she'll slump to the ground.

"Hanna-feels-like-all-the-others!" she blurts.

"I've made up my mind to go over to Hanna," Tzivia said. "I don't want to stay here, even if they kill me. I want to be together with my sister. I won't stay in all this wickedness!"

Daniella turned frightened eyes upon her.

"Tzivia, have you gone out of your mind? Tzivia, for pity's sake!"

"I've already told the Master-Kalefactress about it," she said.

Daniella seized her with both hands: "And what did the Master-Kalefactress tell you?"

"When I have three 'reports' she'll send me to Hanna," Tzivia innocently repeated the Master-Kalefactress's words.

Daniella did not as yet know what "report" meant.

III

Seven o'clock in the morning is Bed-Building Parade in the rosy blocks. Elsa, the Master-Kalefactress, and her staff inspect the beds to see if they have been "built" according to regulation. Here, in the Joy Division, the bed reigns sacred and supreme. And the maidens of paradise are its keepers.

At the foot of each bed is marked the number branded in the flesh of the bed's guardian. And here Elsa has a wide scope to cause things to take such a turn that during Enjoyment Duty the girl won't be able to help getting a "report."

Fifty beds to a block, twenty-five to a wall, opposite each other, and a clear aisle down the centre. At the head of each bed, a narrow closet, for the clothes of the nobility coming here for Enjoyment. High in the closet, a single shelf, for the girl's eating utensils. To ensure the cleanliness of the utensils, every morning at ten o'clock there is Utensil Parade. God help the girl whose utensils show up with so much as a speck, whose spoon is not laid out strictly according to the book, the smell of whose bowl is not entirely to Elsa's taste. Such a thing means: the owner of the utensil has been inconsiderate of the aesthetic sensibilities of her high-born guests, who also avail themselves of the closet. For such a sin Elsa has unique penalties of her own, which sooner or later are sure to impel the girl to a "report."

Very early in the morning, with the first knell of the gong, there is great agitation in the blocks: Bed-Building! Each girl works feverishly, bent over her bed, hands frantic with fear. Will her Bed-Building pass today? Will she succeed? And if she fails?

"Help me, God! Help me, God!" the lips flutter as the hands scramble about building the bed, and the tears drop and are upholstered into the long, narrow death litters.

The bed looks like a narrow, long chest. It is filled with wood shavings covered with a dark grey blanket, the mattress. Over that, a second blanket for covering; and at the head, a pillow-case filled with shavings. To all appearances that is all. But how many blameless budding lives has the bed devoured in the mere building! For it is a solemn duty to build it in strict accordance with the principles of German punctiliousness. And standing firm on the discharge of this duty is Elsa of Düsseldorf.

First of all, the lower blanket—the mattress, that is to say —is required to be smooth as a mirror. Not a dent, not a bulge, evened out as with a carpenter's level. Consequently, first come the shavings, which, from being lain upon day and night, form kinky lumps here and hollow dips there. But this you can't explain to anyone in paradise, for neither Yaga, the Blonde Beast, nor Elsa of Düsseldorf sleeps on wood shavings, nor do they ever "build" a bed. That is done for them by the kalefactresses in attendance upon them.

And now, the strictest regulation of all: the mattress-blanket must be exactly four inches higher than the frame of the chest-bed. Precisely 4.0. Not a hair's breadth more or less. So that together with the upper blanket the "build" should not be more than five inches above the side boards. The inches are punctiliously drawn on each bedpost.

4.0 inches.

The terrifying 4.0 inches of Bed-Building.

Finally, the upper blanket must spread level and smooth over the whole length of the bed, escarp at the pillow and lap over it in two lines—parallel, sharp, angular, like tin sheets. And to crown it all, a horrible death is in store if, God forbid, a hair or wisp of shaving is found on the upper blanket.

THE BED—THE HOLY OF HOLIES! A sign blares the warning from the wall of each block.

Every morning at seven Elsa and her cohort come trooping in for inspection. The girls stand at taut, erect attention, each by the bed of her keeping. The bed now becomes an integral part of her body, a vital organ in which the whole nervous system is concentrated. Her life now folds itself into the dark, narrow bed chest. They become one—the girl and the bed. One number identifies them both. And the heart no longer thumps in the breast, but there, in the long narrow bed. And the terror no longer throbs in the body, but there, in the dark line where the blanket escarps the pillow—the 4.0-inch line.

"Help me, God! Help me, God!" the heart entreats from inside the bed.

Elsa stops by the first bed, goes down on one knee, shuts her right eye, aims her left eye down the row of beds. The pillow-line of the first bed must be perfectly aligned with the pillow-line of the twenty-fifth bed. She's a pure-blooded German, is Elsa of Düsseldorf. She knows what German precision is, and she'll teach it to this shit nation, the Jewish whores.

If a bed is found out of line, Elsa immediately orders the number of the bed entered in the book. Elsa delights in the mere uttering of the order. And while her clerk writes, Elsa eyes her victim with her narrow eye-slits, arms folded across her chest, one booted leg thrust forward, her mouth writhing. She smirks, baring her stubby jags of teeth, whose gaps are blacker than the teeth are white. And if fate has pointed to a beautiful girl—aah! Elsa hates beautiful girls to the death.

After inspection, Elsa assembles the Bed-Building victims and orders them to knee-bend: squat, knees bent, hands clasped around the nape, rump not to dare touch the ground. The girls must sit this way from early morning until Enjoyment Duty at two o'clock, when the Germans come to the Doll House to "enjoy."

After such a knee-bend the girls are incapable of moving an arm or a leg. The whole body is one knot of pain which cannot bear touching. The girls are incapable of straightening

167

their legs, let alone walking. They have to be led. And thus, slumped against their comrades, they are dragged to their beds, to perform their task at Enjoyment Duty.

No wonder, then, that the noble guest later complains to the orderly room: the "number" didn't satisfy him. The Enjoyment was a flop. The girl wasn't sweet to him. Treated him with indifference.

Certainly he took down the number. Here. And he turns the number over to the office.

"Report!"

Bed-Building Parade is followed by other Parades. Eating-Utensil Parade; Smock Parade. To each parade its victims, and Elsa impels her victims to a state where they will bring "reports" on themselves. And so on, and on.

And Elsa of Düsseldorf is not to be sated.

14

ENJOYMENT DUTY.

There is not a sound in the block. The girls sit, each on her bed, legs propped on the floor. Fifty beds, in two single files, with fifty girls seated backs to each other. No one had decreed this seating arrangement. They seem to be sitting this way deliberately, so their glances should not meet. Fear is contagious. Soon they will be called upon to smile. The smile is not optional. The smile attests to the girl's attitude to Enjoyment. Her life depends on the smile. Soon they will be called upon to be happy.

There is not a sound in the block.

For a while yet they are permitted to commune with fear, with this thing about to take place here. Now they are still permitted to feel the horror of what awaits them. And they abandon themselves to the open arms of fear, which any moment will have to give way to the Germans. Soon their faces will wear smiles. The noble German guest hasn't come here to look at sad eyes. He has come to Enjoy! To get his bucketful of joy! That clear to the Doll? If not, he'll make it clear to her! First of all, let's have the number! He wants a copy of the number in his pocket. Just for the hell of it. Afterwards, when he passes by the orderly room, he'll think it over. But just now, with her brand number already jotted down in his pocket, let the Doll be so good as to love him properly! The way he likes it! With gusto! Gay does it! He wants to get his fill of her just the way he washes down a mug of Prussian beer, white foam and all.

Outside, the gong booms—

Two o'clock.

It's time.

There is not a sound in the block. Fifty girls—as if they had nothing to say to each other. Fifty beds—like fifty stools arrayed on the Execution Square before the naked bodies are strapped to them.

Outside, German voices are approaching. Elsa is screeching final orders to the kalefactresses, drowning out the Germans' ribaldry. Maybe that will help draw their attention and serve them notice just who and what she is here. Even Yaga lingers on the square in front of the blocks. They hustle and bustle and shout outside like stage directors before curtain time on opening night. Any moment now the block gate will open, and the Germans will come in.

Fifty beds—like fifty before the firing squad, standing motionless in a straight row, staring into the gun muzzles, waiting for the bullet to pierce the heart—silent. They have nothing to say to each other.

Every day. At exactly two o'clock.

Daniella looks at the back of the girl sitting on the bed in front of her: the thin, blue pinstripes of the smock dazzle her eyes. The girl's hair streams down to her nape as the stripes on her back lift from the smock, up, up, now covering the hair as well, withdraw from the back, hover in mid-air. All at once the stripes look like bars . . . a cage . . . the girl is sitting in a barred cage. . . the stripes on the backs of all the girls suddenly withdraw and are like bars . . . two rows of cages . . . in each cage a girl's back, motionless, waiting for the chief physician to come and perform scientific research on her body . . .

Stillness. As though the air were clogged. The German voices reach in from beyond the block window as though it all were happening far, far away, and they, themselves, were in that far-away. The knells of the gong roll out of the sky under their echoes, as cloaked in long black capes. The knells drift earthward, the trains of their capes trailing across the rooftops and covering the rosy blocks as with a shroud of black. Darkness. But she feels the gong knells are looking in

169

at her through the block window together with the German voices. They guffaw . . . the girls' heads spin before her eyes like wheels . . . wheels of a night tram down Kongressia's drowsing streets . . . wheels of locomotives . . . WHEELS AWAY TO VICTORY! . . . Jeering faces of conductors . . . She is in her room . . . and now she is in Metropoli station among the girls of the transport . . ."*Dani, why are you going away?*" "*To bring you a present, my pet.*" The wheels grind clangorously into rails. Knives cut the wheels—she will grab a knife and slash the German's body when he's lying on her. The knife slashes and rips and the German's blood spurts on to her breasts, over her branded number. Night. Crimson night. The streets of Kongressia are fast asleep, but the iron wheels of the night tram grind with terrific clangour along the tracks. She stabs and slashes with the knife, and the blue inscription FELD-HURE is red, flooded with German blood. Her fingers are sticky with blood and her eyes see the letters FELD-HURE flooded with blood, the way the JUDE branded on the brow of Shlamek's father brimmed over with blood. Blood for blood. German blood—

The door bursts open. The block fills with Germans. Uproar. Commotion. Countless black boots. A seething cauldron. German. Shouts. Guffaws. No more bars. No cages. Everything unloosed. No wheels. The round head of the girl slumped back on the bed-head——

Enjoyment Duty.

At Daniella's bed, the German hangs his jacket in the closet. In the adjacent bed, the girl looks right into the German's eyes. She smiles—but her smile weeps, as though she had drawn it out of a jar of tears where it had been soaking. The girl's eyes rake through the German's countenance, trying to divine as by face-reading: what does this face have in store for her today? Is there a human spark hidden behind it? She searches for the spark. She wants to find it, hold on to it, reach out a hand to it like a drowner. Her life is now in his hands. She now belongs to him, all of her. He will express his opinion about her. His opinion—an irrevocable verdict. Will he sate himself, like the beast gorging down its prey, grunting and going its way, or will he put her on a "report" just as an extra pleasure?

Daniella's ears are clogged. The bawdy German shouts reach into her ears as from a great distance, like the wild echoes of a cannibal chant. She knows her hair is being pulled at, but she feels no pain. Her eyes are shut, but she sees the lacework of the curtains hung over the block windows with the figurettes cut out in their centre. The figurettes are white with daylight. *"German soldiers will teach you!"* Out of the loud debauchery rises the hoarse, heavy voice of the German croaking into her ear. Her eyes are shut. The voice has a rubicund, drunken face, a leather jacket: "13" ... The same curtains ... as in the Research Block windows ... *"German soldiers will teach you! ..."* The face of the Neanderthal mummy is lying on her, pawing her, licking her face. She lies bound as in the cage, knees astraddle, unable to move a limb. Can't escape. Sparks. Yellow sparks spurting from red circles. The mummy covers her. She feels his smell. His mouth is ajar. Huge bare teeth, like a beast's. His fingers dig in to her body like a crab's pincers. The chief physician looks in at her in the cage. His eyes smile benignly. She lies strapped to the table rods. She can't stir. Schultze sends his long cane at her. The rubber tip nears her eye. Any moment and it will pierce her eye, suck out her life. Schultze sniggers. He wears a black SS cap. Schultze—he's the chief physician. His face looks very grave as he turns to the Germans behind him in Yablova woods and says, "The 'Jungs' will be pleased with her." The girls in the cages opposite embroider red blossoms on linen tablecloths. An unfinished blossom—like the smashed head of the history teacher in the blood puddle ... She wants to scream. Her head tosses from side to side, like the girl whose organ was torn out of her and put in the jar. She opens her mouth wide, wants to scream, but cannot. She is afraid. The fear plugs her throat like a cord. Down in her belly a pain flashes like a tongue of flame leaping from an ash pile ... The Slovakian doctor sticks in a hypodermic needle. The blood rises in the glass tube. *"German soldiers will teach you."* *"The 'Jungs' will be pleased with her."* The red blossoms are scattered, as though carelessly strewn on the white tablecloth. *"Dani is like a bud. When she opens, her beauty will take the breath away ..."* *"Of course I said you're my beautiful blossom..."*

On the curtains covering the block windows the sky plays a strange image-game: people running frantically in the thick of a forest ...

In a nearby bed the German gets up, makes ready to leave. The girl's arms, white and naked, cling to him. Her face twists into a smile as her lips whisper, "Please sir, was the gentleman satisfied?"

The German shoves her away, spits, walks off. The girl sits there, her naked white arms hanging spiritlessly from her knees. She looks to him. He is going away, carrying in his pocket the fate of her polluted life. The Execution Square looms before her eyes. She looks, looks. The German is already gone, and she is still looking to him—

Was he? . . .

II

. . . Tonight . . . after the last gong . . . it must be done tonight! Daniella decides.

The block is tidy, hushed, empty, as if there were not a living soul there. Any moment and the lights will go out. Any moment and the last gong will sound. After the last gong, everyone is required to sleep. One of those camp regulations. The Germans are concerned with the girls' welfare. They must be hale and fresh tomorrow at two.

The two rows of beds reach into the centre of the block like two rows of corpses laid out by the walls, feet straight, rigid.

To sleep!

But now, of all times, the Execution Square sprawls before the eyes. Of all times now, when each is alone in her bed communing with herself, the heart takes stock of the day past and senses the dread of the "report" lurking in the morrow.

To sleep! After the last gong everyone is required to sleep. But how subject sleep to German edict? How decree sleep to come and eclipse with its wings the visions of Germans and Execution Square swarming ceaselessly beneath the shuttered eyelids? How make sleep lull the death trepidation of the body?

. . . Though it's only a blind-man's-buff with fate. There are girls here with two "reports." They're called "Luckies." They've been around a long time. They have outlived many girls who got here when they already had their two "reports." In fact, it's a camp tradition that the "Luckies" will live to be liberated. Even so, in their beds at night, they tremble about tomorrow more than the others. They delve and dig and delve some more in the face of the German. Try their hardest to recall his every word, his every gesture, his every

172

glance as he leaves: are they going to live? Was he satisfied? ...

It's easy to believe in the camp tradition when it's not your own life in the balance.

... Tonight! After the last gong, when the lights are out in the blocks. She'll go out to the latrine. From there it's not far to the lake. The water will enfold her. The water will rinse her body and purify it. The water will rinse her eyes and quench the fire raging in her head. She will lie deep, deep on the bottom of the lake, the way she's lying here, on the bed, only there it will be peaceful, soft, free. The lake water won't stop streaming over her naked body and will cleanse it inside and out. She'll be pure, light, free.

Now it's prohibited to leave the blocks. Now, between the second and last gong, it's prohibited even to go to the latrine. The sentry will shoot her and get his bonus—three days' leave. "A doll was making for the barbed wire," he'll report. No, only not to be shot in front of the blocks! ... The girl had lain in front of Block 8 until dawn that time, and her groans all night nearly drove them all crazy. Only not to get shot in front of the blocks ...

Everybody here is going to get "reports." Everybody will be taken to the Execution Square. Not a single one will be left. The Germans will kill them all at the last minute, and no one will ever know what kind of camp there had been here. Tomorrow, the day after, she'll also be taken to Purgation. Where do they take all those tossed on the van? What do they do to them at the place they're taken to? What kind of death is picked out for them there? Tonight! She's not waiting for them to take her to the Execution Square and toss her on the van. It must be tonight! But it won't happen tonight either. She won't carry it through this time, just as she didn't any of the other nights. Like all the other girls, she'll wait till the van comes to take her away. If only Vevke hadn't stopped her from buying the cyanide pills at the shoe-shop canteen, she would have sneaked out to the road between Jew-Quarter 1 and Jew-Quarter 3, and in one of the clefts of the mountain would have swallowed them —and be done with it! How peaceful it was there. So bright. It would have been good just to sit there, in a hidden nook, and look out. If only they had let her live there, she could have gone on staying there for ever. There wasn't a hiding place like it in the whole ghetto. She would sit there, alone.

173

Just she. She would never get tired of sitting there. There is so much compassion and understanding in the crevices of the mountain. She would never forget the mountain for what it had done for her. And when the war ended, she would come out of her hideout and walk all the way to Kongressia. Free over free roads. She would take Moni by the hand and walk back with him to the mountain and show him. Let them all see the mountain that had given her shelter, that had hidden her. Hadn't bawled her out "Yid!" and hadn't run her off. Here, beside the mountain, they would all meet: Harry, papa, mama. She would take them all to Jew-Quarter 3. Better still, she would stand in the soup-kitchen compound and wait there for them to appear. She'd see them in the distance and make out right off which speck was who. She would run to them. The sun would stream in between the high mountain and the low mountain; she would take them to the "plot." The bench Tedek made must still be standing there. She'd offer them some of the red radishes she had planted and tended with her own hands. Then she'd take them to the Centre. Here is Hayim-Idl's "villa" . . . here's the bed she slept in . . . above, on top of the tile stove, under the ceiling, are the written notebooks of her diary, and there, between the cooling box and the wall, under the window sill, is her last notebook. Now she'd also take out the notebooks in which she wrote everything that happened to her—

The last tolls of the gong broke in through the block windows, reminding of the morrow to follow the night. The girls tossed and turned in their beds, and black blankets rose from the beds like phantoms. The knells of the gong rolled out echoes of familiar horror. Suddenly it seemed the closet doors were tearing open and the block filling with German voices. Bedlam. The Germans hang their clothes in the open closets. Two o'clock tomorrow.

. . . Everything that happened to her in the ghetto is written in her diary. And "two o'clock tomorrow"? No one will ever know about that. No one will ever know what happened in this camp. The Germans will "purgate" them all on the Execution Square. No one will survive.

. . . Tonight she'll go to the water! If she'd only bought the tablets. . . . Of course Fella will survive. Fella is a "Lucky." If she could write down what's happening here, maybe Fella would then be able to pass it on. Yaga's promised to take her along to Dresden after the war. But the Germans will probably kill Fella too. No one will get out of here. Elsa will toss Fella into the van—

"Where did they bring you from?"

The voice came from the next bed. The girl lay facing Daniella. She looked at her and repeated the question. "Where did they bring you from?"

The question embeds itself in Daniella's ears. *"Where did they bring you from?"* In the next bed a pair of eyes look to her, waiting for an answer. The same question she heard in the Labour Division on the straw.

"From Jew-Quarter 3," she replied.

The girl in the next bed leaned up.

"I'm from Jew-Quarter 1. Maybe you met my family there? Maybe you know how they're getting along? My name is Shafran. Tzippora Shafran. In the first roundup they separated me from my family. You don't know if any of them have been saved? We used to live at 12 Liberty Square."

Her mind began to reel. The same talk. Each and every place the same thing. The same questions, the same answers.

"No," she said. "I didn't know any of your family. I'm not from there. I wound up there during the war, at my brother's. He also lived in Jew-Quarter 1. His name is Harry Preleshnik."

The girl jumped off her bed, came nearer and studied her face closely.

"Dani?"

Dani . . . Who is this? Daniella searches the face bent over her. Who is she? Where does this girl know her from? Where did they meet? A grey blank hangs over her memory.

"Yes, at home I was Dani."

Tzippora Shafran let herself down on the edge of Daniella's bed. She sank her face into her hands, was silent.

Daniella took a hand from the girl's face. "Who are you?"

Tzippora Shafran was three years older than she, beautiful and charming, of a well-known, cultured Jewish family in Metropoli. Here, in the camp, she was the only survivor of her transport.

Tzippora did not look up. "Harry always used to talk about you at home. He was proud of his golden-haired sister. How I always wanted to meet you. And now we've met. In the Doll House."

The light went out.

To sleep! ...

Outside, a full moon was silvering the electric wall of barbed wire. The rows of narrow white closets at the bed-heads looked like tombstones. Tzippora sat on the edge of Daniella's bed, talking and telling as though someone inside her were seeking self-vindication before another. The sudden meeting with Harry Preleshnik's sister had taken the shrouds off a dead past. She had been deported from the ghetto with her brother Marcel. Here she found out that Marcel was in one of the labour camps in the vicinity. She wanted to help him, was even ready to go to him and bring him bread—but she was afraid. The girls come back from the men's camps with "reports." Going to these camps is as good as going to death. Later she found out that Marcel wasn't there any more. Maybe he had been taken on one of the transports deep inside Germany. "If Marcel died of hunger then I'm to blame. I was a coward. I could have helped—"

... Harry! it bolted in Daniella's mind—maybe Harry is also in one of these labour camps, crying for help! Her life suddenly took on a sacred, sublime meaning. Now she'll be able to stand anything: Harry is waiting for her help ...

"How do you get into the labour camps? How do you get out of here?" Daniella asked impatiently.

"The Germans guarding the camps around here have girls sent to them from Doll House, since they can't relax the guarding of the camps. The area is full of labour camps for Jews, and the girls usually get back with a 'report.' Some don't get back at all. They generally send girls from the new transports. Watch out they don't send y—"

"I'll ask to go! Harry is in a labour camp. I'll look for him! I saw in the Labour Division what hunger is like."

The block looked like a dark ghetto alley. From time to time a moan rose from a bed as out of a ghetto window. The moon embossed the window panes with silver. Gloom and unearthliness were outside the window pouring in long-ing and despair. Someone called from a bed, "Tzippora! Sing something or we'll go crazy!"

Almost every evening Tzippora Shafran sings, and all the girls join in. She is fondest of the lullabies her mother used to sing her as a child. Most of the songs are Hebrew, for Tzippora's mother had been a Hebrew teacher in her youth. The girls in the block, though Hebrew is strange to most of them, have already picked up all the songs Tzippora's mother

176

used to sing as she rocked her to sleep. The childhood melody
hovers among the beds like a mother's soul. Each girl's
mother. And each mother opens her arms toward the bed
of her daughter.

There is no song in Tzippora tonight. This time it is no
longer a melody of yearning alone. This time it is her mother's
breath warm on her face, the way she felt it when she would
lull her to sleep.

Pleading voices carry from the beds:

"Tzippy! Sing something. Please, Tzippy."

Tzippora cannot withstand the entreaties and starts trilling
softly:

> "All the world's aslumber—hush!
> Apple, pear—each in its tree.
> Mama's sleeping, papa too,
> But there's no sleep for my heart and me . . ."

The melody flows, unfurls, drapes a film of gossamer white
over the narrow closets, over the walls; sways on a silvery
horizon, like a bewitched vessel slicing through waves toward
the silver gate of a full moon.

Through the window peer the red lamps glowing over the
barbed wire. Above the watchtower hangs the moon sphere,
like the halo around the head of the tormented Jew of
Nazareth in the images placed in the Polish windows to indi-
cate that here lives a non-Jew.

. . . Just a slice of bread might save Harry . . . she'll
volunteer to go to the labour camps . . . half a bread she'll
surely be able to get hold of . . . Daniella's suffering was
suddenly purified and whitened, like molten gold in the re-
fining blaze of the crucible.

Outside, the night stands beneath the window, bearing
Daniella's fate inscribed and sealed. The night's bare feet are
dusted with moon-silver. Out of the rosy blocks flows a grief-
sodden melody of longing. And the night gathers the melody
up in its bare arms, soars away with it over the block roofs,
beyond the electric barbed wire, and caches it in the safety
of its vaults.

15

WHEN Fella got to the Joy Division, she immediately saw
there was bad business ahead for her. She, Fella, of the Jewish

town of Radno, isn't going to be able to live in the same four walls with Elsa of Düsseldorf. One of them's got to give: either—she, or—Elsa. The place just isn't big enough for both of them. And, since Fella knew, if she aims to live to settle things both with pure-blooded Elsa of Düsseldorf and with the Judenrat gang, she'll have to keep her horns in and her dander down, she immediately upon getting here set about planning how to keep out of Elsa's way, to avoid any run-ins with her. For never so much as now did Fella crave so to live for the day of liberation—of revenge.

That being the case, she first has to get out from under Elsa's thumb. So long as she's got Elsa over her, it's bound to end up in a mess: Fella isn't letting Elsa squash her like a worm. She just won't be able to hold herself back. She'll fly off the handle and paste into the Frankenstein's monster of Düsseldorf and really bitch things up—not only for herself but for all the Joy Division girls clear down through the last transport. The Germans will take it out on them as only they know how. Oh no, she's not taking that on her conscience. So she'd better hurry up and figure something out while she's still got her wits about her, before she's turned into a dummy flesh machine like the rest of the Doll House girls.

And if a way out—then only with old Beelzebub himself and not with any of his junior stooges.

The next day, before the beginning of Enjoyment, as the girls sat trembling on their beds waiting for Duty to start, Fella looked through the window at the German soldiers coming over the bridge toward the square. She sized them up very carefully, as though this time it were she who was doing the picking out of a victim—someone who would be right for her scheme. Suddenly she noticed Yaga, the Camp Commander, walking arm-in-arm with one of the guests—a German officer. Looks to be a boy friend of hers. And right then and there Fella decided: it's this high and mighty swine that's going to help her out.

When the Germans approached the block, Fella quickly hid in the closet by her bed and watched through the chink in the closet door. When she saw her marked guest enter the block, she stepped out of the closet and made, all hips, straight for him.

Fella didn't have to waste words. Her proud, curvaceous body, her exquisite legs, her sparkling rows of smiling teeth,

178

her fiery black eyes—all these spoke for her in a plain language of their own.

The German seized her by the hand, and did not let her pass. Fella flashed him a glance, her shapely mouth pouting with injured innocence.

"Such carryings on for a gentleman?"

The German stood there wide-eyed. For a moment he forgot he was in the Doll House. He had never heard such words here, had never been addressed here this way. Instinctively he blurted, "*Verzeihen Sie*—"

. . . Nice going! Fella thought. Not at all bad to hear in this Doll House a German officer speak up to a Jewish field-whore with "Pray forgive me." Fella linked her arm, grande dame-like, in his, and led him to her bed. They sat down, eyed each other a moment and burst into hearty laughter.

They sat down and chatted away pleasantly. After a short while, the German felt the likes of this had never happened to him here. This freedom in Fella's manner, her ability to rouse in him the manly sense of honour—and in a place like this, when all around him soldiers were wallowing like swine in mud—all this opened up in him latent, forgotten feelings, which elevated him above his surroundings. Needless to add, Fella's beauty, charm, and audacity were of no little help. And above all, her expert knowledge of the ways and by-ways leading into the male heart.

Fella now called into play all the tactics of female strategy. And it was not long before the German was completely in her power, like a snake under the spell of a charmer. He spoke up as though making a confession, "Yes, I came to the Doll House for what all the others come for. I intended to spend a little time here. But I've found something loftier."

. . . Not bad! Fella considered. Not bad at all! And when she felt the barometer of her success was high enough, she decided it was time to lay her cards on the table. Have to play it quick. Before you know it time's up and the chance in a million is down the drain. So she said with her usual simplicity and frankness, "Now tell me, lover boy, do you want my body manhandled like all the others, or do you think it's worth having all for yourself?"

The German gaped as though jolted out of a dream. He felt himself cornered. Fella's question cut him down from his romantic flight back to reality.

"I'd completely forgotten," he stammered.

"Suppose you thought you were sitting with some chippy on Unter den Linden back in Berlin!" Fella drew tighter on her bowstring.

"This camp is under Gestapo jurisdiction," the German thought aloud. "There is nothing to be done there. But what I could do is try to arrange for you to become kalefactress, so you'll be free from Enjoyment Duty."

Fella shook her head.

"First of all, nothing in the world will get me to do any kalefactressing under Elsa. Kalefactress, that means butchering the girls. And I'd sooner die myself than kill someone else. Second of all, camp law doesn't allow beautiful girls to be kalefactresses." And while explaining all this she got up, coquettishly projecting the curves of her body, and continued, "You don't really think, do you, that this body isn't cut out for anything better than kalefactress in the Doll House?"

The German chuckled. His eyes roved over the beckoning mould of her body, pausing at the bold arcs where smock overlapped bosom. He reached out and drew her down beside him. Fella was wide awake. Fella knew how time ran out during such love talk. She continued to prod, "Well, what'll it be?"

"I don't know what to do. Honestly," the German answered anxiously.

She lay back across the width of the bed. Her long, graceful legs—Fella's tried and true weapon—stood bare up to her thighs. She felt his eyes on the undraped apples of her knees, sat up again. Looking him straight in the eye she said, "All right then, come and take what you came for, like all the others! Tomorrow somebody else'll be sitting in your place. Guess he'll also say, 'In you I found something lo-o-ftier.' Excuse me if I was wrong about you!"

The German was in a vice. It did not occur to him to think of the trap into which a Jewess had suddenly led him. He did not stop to think: why was he letting himself become so involved here? Why doesn't he "take what he came for," like all the others, and be done with it—just as Fella had artfully told him. And perhaps it is because she had said it to him so simply and ingenuously that he felt himself so obligated.

A strange whim of Eros in the German Doll House.

"I'm ready to help you, if you'll just tell me how," he said.

Actually, that was all Fella was waiting to hear. She drew herself up and spoke to him with all her heart:

"I'm good at housekeeping and cleaning rooms. I was working at it when I was still a kid. Maybe one of the Germans here in camp can use a maid."

The German suddenly slapped himself on the brow, let out "Idiot!" and hurried from the block.

Her eyes followed him from behind the curtain of the block. He was heading for the Camp Commander's quarters. Well, kid, Fella thought, you've made it half-way. Now you've only got to make it the other half. And though Fella was not accustomed to turning to God—she had a long account with Him since her early childhood—she now joined her hands as in prayer and her lips breathed, "Help me, God! If you think you can go along with me now, I promise I'll become a good girl after the war. Please help me get out of camp. I've got to square it with those Judenrat scum. I'll polish off that Monyek with my own hands. I've got to do it! I've just got to! And Elsa . . . Just help me get out of here. But if you don't feel like giving me a hand, all I ask, dear God, please don't mess it up for me. Please don't butt in. I'll pull it off myself. That's all I ask: just don't mess me up with my German!"

Through the window she saw the Camp Commander coming out of her quarters arm-in-arm with the German. He is talking energetically to her, obviously trying to convince her. They are coming to the block.

Yaga sized her up. The German's eyes smiled with satisfaction. Apparently, Fella met with Yaga's approval for she told her to follow her immediately.

God granted Fella's prayer. She was accepted as maid in the Camp Commander's quarters.

When Daniella later arrived at the Joy Division, Fella stood by her like a devoted sister. Fella never forgets for a moment that a great miracle has befallen her here. The Camp Commander is pleased with her. Fella knows how to win the heart of the German Beast. And when Yaga has had a few drinks, she pours her heart out to Fella as to a close friend. Fella has already heard from Yaga the most intimate stories of her life: about her beau, the commander of nearby Camp Niederwalden, who is two-timing her; about her youth, which she spent in a whorehouse in Dresden. In her drunkenness she often sympathizes with Fella for having been born a Jewess.

181

If not, she wouldn't be a prisoner but—take it from Yaga—commander of a German concentration camp. She'd have seen to that. Fella is her only true-blue friend in the whole wide world.

Every morning Fella comes hurrying to Block 5 to help Daniella at her "Bed-Building." An extra pair of hands on the other side of the bed is a real godsend. And Daniella's bed is always ready first, after which Fella and Daniella check to see that all the other "bed-builds" are uniform.

And Fella became the guardian angel of the girls of Block 5.

16

. . . SOMETHING terrible was in the air this morning. All Daniella's senses were keyed up. She sensed it as tangibly as the imminence of an Aktion is felt in the ghetto, even though the Germans have not given the slightest indication of it. She was lying on her bed, her ears pricked for the slightest rustle. There was something different about this morning—suspicious, ominous. Something was going to happen. She could sense it like one sensing a lurking danger, though not seeing it face to face.

In the block everyone was still asleep, yet she felt the gong should long since have rung. It frightened her, this holiday atmosphere, their still being asleep. Why was the waking gong so late today?

Since getting the notebook and pencil from Fella, she wakes early. With the others still asleep, it's the best time to pull out the notebook and pencil from under the wood shavings in the bed—and write. Write.

This morning is different from all the others. The muffled sounds outside are suspicious, sinister. In the next bed Tzippora Shafran wrestles in her sleep. Her face goes through contortions, her neck writhes, she groans and snorts as though someone were strangling her in a dream.

Since they first met, Tzippora has changed completely. The "Luckies" of the block buzz among themselves that Tzippora has gone out of her mind. She's not the first such a thing has happened to here. They're afraid the Slovakian doctor will notice and lock her up in the KB-isolation among

182

the venereals. Lately Tzippora has been roaming about the camp like an outsider; as if the Doll House regulations no longer applied to her. The luck which had been with her this far now suddenly deserted her. All at once she got two "reports" on two consecutive days. And ever since, she's been going about everything indifferently, carelessly. She doesn't even sing any more. Her mouth is clamped. All she lets out once in a while is "I killed Marcel," and she again clamps her mouth.

. . . Something is coming off outside. Elsa's voice carries from somewhere. Kalefactresses sprint past the block. There's definitely something up. She felt the danger stalking her from an ambush somewhere.

The girls are still fast asleep, as if no power on earth could wake them. But no sooner will the first gong sound than they will all spring out of bed as one: Bed-Building! That's the way it is every morning. Suppose the war ended suddenly, the Germans fled by night, there was no more waking gong —would the girls go on lying this way for ever?

The bustle outside mounts. What are they doing there? Fella had told her confidentially that they might be shifting the camp nearer to the front. Fella knows. You can rely on her. Yaga must have let something slip. No! This time she's not waiting to be transferred again. She'll put an end to it here. She's already been in almost all the Jew-camps in the area. To talk to the prisoners is impossible. Even to see them is out of the question. The Germans live outside the barbed wire and there's no chance of getting inside to the prisoners. She'll never find Harry. Was all her torture—

The block gate is torn open. First to come in is Elsa, the braided knout in one hand and a white slip of paper in the other. Kalefactresses search among the numbers of the bed-posts. They go about their work swiftly, without a sound, like demons. They sweep from bed to bed, and are approaching hers. With both hands she clutches the notebook and pencil under her back. She knows they are coming for her now. It is she they are after. No question about it now. She foresensed it. But before it frightened her as a general danger, threatening everyone. Now it is concentrated, poised like a spear right at her. Only at her. She's the victim this time. This time the eyes will all be looking through the barbed wire—at her. Under her back her hands pressed on the notebook and pencil. No time to hide them. The kalefactresses look at her bed number. In a flash, waves of questions and answers billow and break in her mind: where did she get the notebook? Fella. They'll kill her anyway, but she's not mentioning Fella's name. The kalefactresses are entering the passage beside her bed. They're near her. She's ready. Queer how calm she is. She'll never give Fella away. She is calm. Her eyes close. Death. That's how it feels . . .

The kalefactresses tear the blanket off Tzippora, drag her by the hair. Tzippora does not utter a sound, lets them do as they please with her. Elsa stands, hands folded across her chest, looking directly at her glazed eyes. Tzippora is silent, and Elsa is silent. Both look at each other, one at the eyes of the other, mute. But they appear to be conversing in an esoteric language of terror.

Elsa goes—and Tzippora goes in her tracks. No one ordered her to follow Elsa. She goes. Behind her—the kalefactresses. The procession leaves the block.

Daniella lies motionless. The wall opposite bends forward together with the narrow closets along it. Any moment and they'll topple over. The foreposts of the beds opposite together with the white numbers on them trundle quickly after each other, like advertisement flash cards in a show window, whose source is never exhausted and whose end has no limit.

Some of the girls jump out of their beds, flit back and forth past Tzippora's bed. Everything is happening as under water. She hadn't heard Tzippora scream. She doesn't remember hearing a sound out of her. The whole thing happened as in a vacuum. They've taken her out of the block, but the vacuum remained after them, filling out the whole block. Girls scurry about, turn to each other, appear to be talking, but she hears nothing. She goes on lying there, hands clutching the notebook and pencil beneath her back. They've led Tzippora from the block—and the first gong hasn't sounded yet. Something terrible is going to happen this morning. Tzippora didn't scream. Everything happened with such dazzling speed, such terrifying silence.

All look at Tzippora's vacant bed:
Elsa has been in the block! . . .
When did it all happen? . . .
Who saw it? . . .
What did Elsa say? . . .
What's going to happen this morning? . . .

Terrified eyes blink, stare. Maybe they've taken her to the KB! Maybe the Slovakian doctor got wind of Tzippora's state . . .

Girls scamper by, look with horror at Tzippora's vacant bed. Now she won't be able to hide the notebook. Why did they take Tzippora? It was for *her* they came! What if they found the notebook on her? And what if they come back again! She doesn't want to go on living, anyway. Why was she so afraid, then?

She pulled her hands out from behind her back—empty. She didn't feel them, just as she didn't feel the rest of her body.

The boom of the first gong shook the block walls.

II

Ten stools stood lined up on the empty Execution Square. Their quadrangular tops gaped empty at the sky. Waiting. The forelegs of the stools were glaringly angular in their starkness.

Opposite, across the Execution Square, the prisoners of the Labour Division now clustered into a huge mass of gaping eyes. The kalefactresses' bludgeons rose and fell on the skulls in the rear ranks. Eyes were agape—not in fear of the Execution Square, but in fear of the kalefactresses' bludgeons: see, they're watching! They're looking! Ten stools right in the middle of the Execution Square, and their tops are empty and facing the sky! Won't the kalefactresses see for themselves: they're looking right at the stools! They don't take their eyes off the stools! If the kalefactresses please, they can even count the chairs: one . . . two . . . three . . . Won't the kalefactresses see how they're looking there and counting, and please not beat them over the head with the clubs!

The van rolled in through the gate, and turned with its back to the Execution Square. The driver's head leaned out of the window. With one hand he manipulated the steering wheel, backing the van to the right spot, to facilitate the loading. The driver hopped down out of the cab, looked the van over with the professional air of an expert driver pulling up exactly at the loading point to spare the porters extra bother. The dark back opening of the van was now directly in line with the row of stools. The driver shoved his SS cap off his brow back on his head, took the cigarette that was perched on his ear, lit it, leaned back against the fender, crossing one leg over the other, inhaled a lungful of cigarette smoke and looked indifferently toward the row of empty stools as he let out a deep, sleep-seeking yawn.

"*During Purgation you'll see how stuffed they are . . .*" The host of bulging eyes on the other side of the Execution Square now merged into a single pair of eyes. "*My name is Renya. Renya Zeidner . . .*" The scathing hatred of all the eyes now converged into one pair of eyes. "*Our bread! . . . Our margarine! . . . It's our lives they're fattening themselves on.*" Renya Zeidner's eyes don't stop glaring at her with hate and loathing. Daniella's played her false. Renya had believed her, trusted her right from the start. But Daniella let her down. She double-crossed her. She left her for the Doll House, where they gorge themselves on the soups and marmalade of the Labour Division. Now, with the trap about to spring, she feels lonely and forsaken. But now no one's going to feel sorry for her. Let her suffer! The time will come for each and every one in Doll House! They'll all gets theirs on the stools! And we, the Mussulmanesses of the Labour Division, will always look through the barbed wire and watch them "purgate" the fat bodies which had stuffed themselves on our bread, on our marrow!

Daniella could not stand to look at the other side any more. She turned her head.

On this side stood girls clad in clean blue pin-striped camp smocks; on the other side a nondescript clump whose tatters fused into one long rotting rag hung out on the wire barbs. A blurred clump, colourless and featureless, limbs and faces indistinguishable from each other. The Doll House girls looked across to the other side, the way relatives look over the rim of an immense mass grave at the exhumed skeletons. Any particle of this blurred decay may be your sister.

Daniella could not stand to look at the other side any more. She looked away—

And saw them:

Marching. Faces to the Execution Square. Marching nearer and nearer.

At the head marches Elsa. Behind her—nude girls goose-stepping in single file.

The sky was dreary, naked. It lay all drawn into the Execution Square, as though outside here there were no sky.

186

To the right of each girl marched a kalefactress with a solemn, festive bearing, like a bridesmaid escorting a bride to the canopy. Elsa's slashed cheek looked from the distance as though half a mask had slipped from her face. The flesh between the crude stitchings now flushed blood red, appearing like a wound sawed into the flesh. The other half-face was taut, festive, solemn. The boot tops sparkled their Sabbath best on her feet, and near her right boot dangled the tail of her braided knout.

First in line was Tzivia of Chebin. She looked as though it were all still a great enigma to her. It was obvious she had not learned anything, hadn't become any the wiser here, in the Doll House, and her innocence hadn't been diminished one bit. As though she were not being led now, naked, from Elsa's chamber, but were stepping thus directly from the Daughters of Jacob night school in Chebin. Her petite, cameo body radiated chasteness and purity—not touched. Her stubborn, infantile innocence shielded her as a tough shell around the kernel of a nut. There was no alternative but to crush the shell into its sealed pith.

Round about, along the wire strands, rows of eyes were strung like beads around the neck of the Execution Square.

By the stools stood Elsa, arms folded across her chest—silent; from the watch-towers the machine-gun muzzles looked silently down; the roofs of the rosy blocks also looked on silently. All must watch the purgation of the sinners of Doll House—and be silent.

Tzippora stands at her stool. Her face doesn't show any change. No change shows in the face of any of them. They stand at the stools, stony, silent, as if unaware of what is about to happen to them. They—the lode-point of all this silence—do not dare ruffle the awesome stillness prevailing here for the occasion of their death.

From somewhere across the sky comes pitching down the last knell of the gong.

. . . Someone else will lie in Tzippora's bed tonight. Probably one of the Blossom Platoon. She, Daniella, standing outside the Execution Square, is now much more terrified than those standing at the stools. Everyone around her here is more terrified than those at the stools. Doesn't Tzippora see death enveloping her naked body as they see it from here, on the outside? Doesn't Tzippora feel anything any more?

187

The Germans arrived at the Square. They strode augustly in, fully conscious of their self-importance, bringing death in their company. They halted some distance from the stools. Death stepped out of their midst and continued to the stools. The Germans followed his steps with their eyes.

Now the kalefactresses went to work. They began strapping the girls to the stools—hands to the forelegs, feet to the rear legs. Elsa signalled with her knout down across the back of a kalefactress for Purgation to begin. The bludgeons rose in unison and in one cadence cut into the naked bodies.

The stillness exploded like a paper bag. Shrieked the barbed wires and shrieked the eyes strung out on them; shrieked the high heavens and shrieked the block rooftops. Fear wept in the Execution Square and death, too, wept.

That's that.

The Germans left the Square like sated guests leaving a banquet hall. Death tailed after them.

The girls were tossed into the van. The driver slammed the tailboard shut. The stools now looked emptier than before. The shrieks which had erupted from them soared off, vanished together with the lives of the girls, leaving the stools in the centre of the Square drained as bottles on a table after a sumptuous feast.

The motor started up and the van took off, leaving behind a singeing smell. Up the road, it turned into the Labour Division to pick up, in passing, the girls whom Hentschel the Moon is now sending into the blue to help build a highway.

17

THE line extended through the whole half of the partitioned block. The girls stood in single file, waiting to be examined. All the Doll House girls have to pass Health Parade once a week, each block on its scheduled day, in numerical order.

Today it's Block 5.

The KB block is partitioned in two. In one section, which is sealed off, they put the girls who contract venereal disease during Enjoyment Duty. From there the girls are sent to the hospital. But no one sent there has ever yet come back.

The KB block is on the outskirts of the camp, beyond the latrine and beyond the rosy blocks. Opposite arches the bridge patrolled by an SS sentry armed with a machine-gun. Actually, the block is intended to serve as hospital for the camp girls—hence its name, KB.[1] But in this camp no one has ever yet taken sick—except, of course, the infected. When the Slovakian doctor does discover a sick girl, she is immediately locked up with the infected in the isolated half of the KB, and together with the infected is sent to the hospital—like them, never to return.

Today it's Block 5.

The girls stand in single file, naked. Near the window, at a small white table, sits the Slovakian doctor, before her a sheet of paper to enter the numbers of the infected. The doctor's eye is glued to the black microscope tube. The examinee stands before the table, surrounded by a semicircle of KB kalefactresses. Along the wall stretches a mute line of naked girls. Their eyes all watch.

The examinee before the table looks at the glass slide fixed beneath the lens of the black microscope. There, on the slide, is smeared her life. There, on the slide, her soul quivers like a fish on the hook. Will the smear of her own, her life on the slide now give her away? Will the moisture of her own belly now hand her over to death? Any second and the doctor's head, bent over the black instrument, will straighten up. Will she motion for the next girl to step up for examination, or will she flash a glance at the number branded on her breast and immediately bend with the pencil over the white sheet beside the microscope?

Outside, by the second fence ranging along the barbed wire, squat some girls of the Blossom Platoon tending the flowers. They chatter loudly, resonantly, carefreely. Their jabber carries through the open window like the insistent buzzing of spring-heralding flies, like winged greetings from rustic dawns and rolling meadows. The voices flutter over the heads of the naked girls; around the black instrument under the grim, bent-over à-la-garçon head of the doctor. The droning prattle flits about in the empty space separating the waiting girls from the white table, skips over the stiff shoulders of the kalefactresses, whose faces like masks reveal no thoughts, skims down the opaque partition, and lights upon the knob of the door which closes behind the infected and opens to them again when the black van comes for them.

[1] KB: Kranken Bau, i.e., hospital.

189

Daniella looks out of the window. The girls of the Blossom Platoon have red kerchiefs on their heads. They squat over the flower beds, trimming the blooms growing above or out of line. The beds must grow straight, even, and perfectly rectangular. The flower bed must look like a stream of red poured into a rectangular tin pan.

Daniella looks out of the window. The red-kerchiefed heads of the Flower Attendants suddenly seem like deviant flowers. They just beg pruning: they disrupt the rectangular symmetry of the bed.

. . . The Blossom Platoon girls will probably be the last survivors here. Maybe they'll even be around at liberation. Elsa picked them for the job. When they got here they had diamond rings hidden in their mouths, and that's how they bought themselves off. The gold chain and the locket are hidden in the bed, under the wood shavings. *"Get rid of that shit! . . ."* She really squeezed through that one. What'll happen to the Blossom Platoon girls when the camp is transferred? Now luck's on their side and they outlive the others. But whenever there's a vacancy in one of the rosy blocks, they take a Blossom Platoon girl, anyway.

No! She won't touch the locket! She came home from school. Lunchtime. The dishes were already set on the table. Papa got up from his chair, came over to her seat, stood behind her: "Close your eyes and don't peek, Dani!" She felt his fingers on her neck. He slipped the locket on, a present for her thirteenth birthday. He kissed her on the nape, where the chain clasped, right where the cut of Elsa's knout hurt most. "All right, Dani," he said. "Now open your eyes!"

She opened her eyes.

The line moves up to the table. The examined girls run from the block barefooted, camp smocks in their hands, gratified, silent. The Flower Attendants move gradually away from the window. The echo of their chatter now tapers in like the waning buzz of a departing fly. The examinee suddenly got a resounding slap in the face from the doctor: she didn't double over properly while she was being examined. She wanted to fool the doctor, to keep the swab from penetrating deep enough, so the moisture of her belly shouldn't give her away. The slap smarts on all the faces. At the distance it hurts much more, for the fear of the slap is more painful than the slap itself. The bowl of tinted water almost topples over. The doctor is riled. And when the Slovakian doctor is riled, the fear intensifies in the lined-up girls. Those yet to be examined look daggers at the girl who had dared resort to such a trick to save her life and thereby annoyed the doctor. At least if she were last in line it wouldn't concern them.

. . . Fella taught her how to handle Enjoyment Duty, and how to avoid infection. First of all, she must rush out to the German. She herself must present him with her body—then it will never occur to him to "report," even if she does later disappoint him. She can never compare to Fella. Fella is of a different mettle. Sturdy, tough, afraid of nothing. Not like her. She's a weakling. She can't help it. She's just made that way. Even Fella's story about the German officer is still beyond her. She'd never have dreamed it was possible even to dare speak that way to a German. None of the girls would have had the guts. If she didn't know what "Enjoyment" is like, she might be able to believe Fella's story. No! She could never have dared. She doesn't even dare imagine such a thing.

The SS sentry on the bridge leans over the wooden railing, tosses bits of bread to the two white swans gliding across the lake. The line moves closer to the table. The girls' naked arms are like long necks of white swans— *Schoolboys and schoolgirls, now on their summer vacation, take frequent walks in the city park. Some lean over the wooden bridge on the lake and toss bits of bread to the snow-white swan gliding across the mirror of water* . . . Reesha Meyerchik won first prize, but the principal said that her description of the swan was better than Reesha's composition about the Baltic Sea. "*To My Gifted Daniella—From Your Brother Harry.*" It was the bronze plaque that saved her life in Yablova market. "Always write only beautiful things in this diary," Harry had said. Now he's in some camp deep inside Germany.

The kalefactresses put a new girl at the table. The two gliding swans are framed in the KB window, float in a pair across the gloss of lake. Behind them—the bridge . . . the bridge! the same bridge! . . . *She is on an unknown lake shore. The swan twins. A brace of swans float toward her. Harry stands wrapped in white, gaping with glazed eyes. She's being chased. The swans spread white wings. She runs toward them—*

Two kalefactresses seize her by the arms: the girl ahead

of her at the table is almost done; Daniella must stand by. The doctor peers into the microscope. The *à-la-garçon* hair on her bent head is greyish-black, like cinders. Her bare nape is reddish, clipped man-style. The nape flesh exudes fear, as though everybody in the world didn't have napes. The black microscope tube is round, like the black SS cap of the chief physician in the Research block.

The girl up at the table looks intently at the slide lying under the lens of the instrument: is her body-smear about to turn her over to death? . . .

The girl's eyes blink. Stare and blink.

The head straightens up from the instrument. A flick of the finger—the girl is gone. Nothing now stands between Daniella and the *à-la-garçon* head. She's looking her over. Does she recognize her? Oh, God! The doctor's mouth is like the mouth of a fish. Its corners arch all the way down. Why is she staring like that? She must have recognized her! Any second and she'll order her to the other side of the partition. Maybe the infected do live on in the hospital? The colour of the tinted water in the bowl blends with all the objects scattered about on the table. From everything and everywhere the fish mouth stares back at her. There's no escaping it. What schemes is the fish mouth clamped around now? Why is she staring at her like that? What does she see on her body?

The upper arc of the doctor's mouth slowly rises. A smile. "Such a tan of a body! Just like an SA man's uniform! What eyes! What a lush figure! Step up, whore, and let me look you over!"

. . . She didn't recognize her! Just don't let her remember. Please, God!

The doctor's hands pass the swab across the slide, dip the swab into the tinted water in the bowl and again daub it on the slide, not taking her eyes off Daniella's body. Oh God, please don't let her remember! She's liable to take it out on her now for the kick in the belly. *"Such a blossom you send to the quarry?"* Harry always called her "my lovely blossom." Fella warned her to watch out not to get infected. What's on that strip of glass? The *à-la-garçon* head peers at it with one eye through the black tube. Daniella can't see anything there. An empty strip of glass, but she feels that the doctor is now peering into her belly, though she's standing away and her belly is closed. *To watch out . . .* Watch out

192

how? Fella can do it. Fella can do anything. What is there, on the other side of the partition? Will Fella remember to take the notebook and locket from under the wood shavings? Fella could turn them over to her parents after the war. The doctor's nape is clipped like a man's. The kalefactresses now hold the arms of the girl behind her. Once the head lifts from the microscope, she'll be stood here in her place. The same bridge! Where have the swans disappeared? The lake is empty. The head straightens up. The eyes pierce her flesh. Just like a fish mouth. *"A body tan just like the uniform of an SA man . . ."* Only don't let her recognize her! Please God! . . .

The doctor flicks her finger.

. . . She's well! Free! She felt that deep inside her someone is very very happy.

II

Daniella was hardly out of the KB when she ran into Fella waiting for her near the block. Daniella was taken aback by Fella's grave expression. It wasn't like Fella to hang around idle in the middle of a work day. Oh no, Fella hadn't lost her Function!

"Are you off from work now, Fella?" she asked hesitantly.

"Have to get right back to work. Come, walk me to the camp gate."

Daniella let out a sigh of relief: so it isn't that! The fright of the examination must have mixed her all up.

After the session in the KB, the camp suddenly looked different. Freer. The mile-long camp road now seemed endless. After the flat, opaque wall opposite the eyes in the block, the sky above the parade ground suddenly looked like—a sky: tall, unbounded. The walls of the barbed wire now seemed low and insignificant against the skyline. From Block 8 girls rushed out to the lake, carrying their eating utensils to scrub and rinse for Utensil Parade. Light now poured all over the parade ground. Beside Block 7 girls were shaking out their blankets. Two girls to a blanket, one on this side, one on the other, holding the blanket by the corners. The muffled snaps of the blankets recalled: balconies on which bedding was shaken out; backyards, windows;

193

homesteads abustle with housewifely diligence. A summer-morning idyll.

The girls of Block 8 run to the lake in bare feet. The sun slivered between their running legs as if they were splashing through puddles of quicksilver. For a moment it all looked like a summer camp somewhere in a sun-endowed corner of creation.

"They're sending some girls to Niederwalden labour camp tomorrow," Fella was saying. "If you want to know something, I wasn't going to tell you. But I just found out Yaga's going too—to her beau, the Camp Commander. If you're dead set on it, I'm game for swinging it with Yaga again to tear up the 'report' you'll get there. Honey, you sure have got it bad."

She leaned against Fella's side and took her arm. She walked like a patient being led by a healthy person. The smock was unbuttoned on her body, and her shoes hung by their laces from the other hand. She hadn't quite finished dressing from the examination. She felt the camp earth under the bareness of her feet and her soul sucked in the air of this very earth. She said, "I'd never forgive you if you didn't tell me."

"Forgive, hell! It's plain crazy, I say. If Yaga wasn't going I'd never let you put yourself up again. Even if I knew they were moving the camp tomorrow."

By the lane to the Science Institute, the Flower Attendants were watering the outside flower beds from rose sprinklers. Entry inside the barbed wire ringing the Institute is prohibited to them. The Institute "nurses" who handle the Experiment-Units also tend the flowers growing inside. The Institute proper is not visible from the outside, the way the skull is not apparent under an elaborate hair-do. The Institute is tucked deep back in the lane, steeped in flowers and foliage. Only a little sign on the barbed wire gate at the head of the lane announces: INSTITUTE FOR HYGIENE AND SCIENTIFIC RESEARCH.

"I'll have to get hold of half a bread," Daniella said. "I'll be able to pay it back during the week from my bread ration."

"I've found out that the Jew-camp in Niederwalden is in the same building as the German Quarters." Fella continued. "Maybe you can pick up some more dope from the Jew-Chief or any Functionary hanging around the camp during the day. I'll work on Yaga. Maybe she'll go crazy and even want to help you. I'll try to set the thing up right. But remember, you're playing with death. You don't know how to handle the Germans. There's just no counting on you."

"I've nothing to lose," Daniella said softly.

"Stop pampering yourself! You're not an only child here! If you watch your step in Enjoyment and steer clear of Elsa, we'll get to Kongressia together yet. You'll see what a time we'll have after the war. The blood will run like water from the Judenrat heads."

Daniella halted by the end of the road. Here the blocks ended. Fella turned toward the inner camp gate.

"I'll drop in before the last gong." Fella again turned her head in walking.

And she was gone.

III

The place where she was standing was paved with square stones. She sat down on the pavement and began lacing her shoes. *Only no thinking about tomorrow!* she pleaded with herself. *Just not to think about it.*

Ahead, the camp road cut black between the two rows of pink blocks. From here the camp looked altogether different —new and strange. As though she were now seeing it for the first time. From this spot she had had her first view of the camp. Now she knows what goes on up there, in the blocks. Everything there is kneaded in with her life. She knows it all as she knows the smell of her own body, the nails of her fingers. She knows the earth there. The flowers. The windows. The block walls and everything happening between them. She knows the bridge arching over the lake, the iridescence of the water and the shadow-black of the SS sentry pacing up and down the bridge. Still, from afar, it's all so strange and new. As if her senses had suddenly gone awry; as if she had suddenly lost her bearings. Like one jolting to a stop on a fully lit square of his home town at night: he knows the place, he always passes it on the way home, yet suddenly doesn't know what corner of the square he's standing on.

This is the pavement she sat on when she got here. How is it that she doesn't recognize the place? It's as vivid in her memory as when she first saw it. But it looks so different

195

—so strange and new. Here's the square on the right—empty . . . it's always on the left! She always sees it from up by the blocks. How is it that she doesn't recognize it any more? As though it weren't in its proper place. That time, when she first came into camp, it looked like a neat, fenced tennis court. It looks one way from here, altogether different from up there.

The dual sensations, of then and now, give the place a double appearance, each distinct from the other. She looks about and can't make out where she is.

From the kitchen block they were lining up steaming soup cauldrons. Soon they'll be carrying the cauldrons into the blocks. Noon. She got up. The stones in the square were neatly and punctiliously laid out. On the right, the road wound toward the Labour Division. Hentschel the Moon is carrying on with the construction of the camp there. At the beginning, Hentschel must have supervised the work here. Right here girls must have scraped their shovels clean, carried railroad tracks from place to place. How many thousands of girls did the black van haul away from here before this little tract was inlaid with stones? How many Mussulmanesses were burned alive before these rosy blocks were up? How much blood of schoolgirls has gone into the sprouting of one single crimson blossom?

She walked up the path to the blocks.

She was looking toward the Labour Division. *"They're buildin' them a highway in heaven. Step right into the van, mein Liebchen, and give 'em a hand. Just don't forget to mention that you graduated at Master-Builder Fritz Hentschel's."* The Moon's little jokes, there. He must have spoofed the same way right here, when his Baustelle was here. Will anyone ever record how many girls have crawled into the van here to help build a highway in heaven? Tomorrow she must volunteer for the Germans at Niederwalden. The whole thing now seemed so pointless and just too much for her. All at once she was seized with longing for all those who had once been here and were no more.

On the horizon, a white cloud tapered down into the red lines of the flower beds. *"There's just no counting on you, Daniella. You don't know how to handle the Germans."* Where was she to get half a bread now?

She went up the path to the blocks.

196

18

"HEY, Medic! Get over here!"

Harry stepped from behind the block gate, where he had edged his head out to see. He came out like a Jew in the ghetto during an Aktion after the Germans have discovered the hole where he was hiding.

"Load the shit up!" the SS man commanded.

The van was parked at the door of the Carrion Shed. When Harry heard the rumble of the approaching van he couldn't restrain himself and rushed from the sick bay to the block gate to peer, to see off for the last time the bones of Zanvil Lubliner. As though, if he neglected to do so, Zanvil might miss it there; or, doing so would make it easier for Zanvil where they are taking him.

The SS driver spotted Harry's head peering from behind the block gate, called him over, lowered the tail-board of the van, issued his order, and made for the German Quarters.

The van was covered with black tarpaulin. The interior was deep and dark. Up in front, opposite the opening, lay a heap of skeletons, naked bones. The heap was neatly stacked, not sprawled, but expertly pyramided like a pile of potatoes in the cellar of a methodical farmer—broad at the base and peaked at the top. Most of the van floor still looked stark bare. This floor must still pick up much "shit" from many camps today. Therefore, the loading has to be intelligent, expert.

The skeletons lie naked. A knotted mound of arms and legs. No telling whether they are women's or men's. Bones. Uncountable bones. Even the heads look like longish bones.

The corpses of his own Carrion Shed—them he knows. Knows when they died and how they died. Only a day or so ago many of them had come to him to the sick bay. He remembers their voices, though now they are silent. He remembers how each one had cheeped to him only yesterday. He even remembers the bruises and festers on their bodies. And those who didn't come to the sick bay any more—he also knows how they died. Even those who were brought back dead from the Baustelle—he knows how they died, too;

197

how they crumpled, shovel in hand, to the ground of the Baustelle and even the Kapo's blows couldn't get them up.

The corpses of his own Carrion Shed—them he knows. As he knows the air and smell of his camp.

Unlike those, piled up in the dark there, deep inside the van. They give off a strange, alien air, as if they had brought with them the smell of their alien camps. They are near to you, very near, yet strange. You seem to be of the same breed, you look just like them, yet they are a revelation to you. Like fallen denizens of remote planets with whom you've come together on alien soil.

You look at them and ask yourself: how did they die, and how had they lived before that? What kinds of torment had they been through there? What does the camp they were brought from look like? And what did they themselves look like? What kind of accent did they have and what language did they speak?

Here, in the van parked on your own parade ground, they look like fantastic guests, like corpses of distinction. First, because they have been brought from the outside, from beyond the barbed wire, from a mysterious somewhere which you cannot plumb, though you know it exists, just as the inhabitants of one planet know of the existence of another planet, yet cannot visualize what it's like there.

Death is everywhere the same. But the life up to death varies. On the mask of the dead face we seek the traces of the lived life; it's not the death in the corpse's face that frightens us, but the life that had animated it. We seek that life, try to visualize it, want to see it—though it frightens us in the absence.

Odd. Even on the knotted, entangled bones of Mussulman skeletons you seek the traces of their previous Mussulmanic life. What did this life look like? In what sort of blocks did they breathe? What kind of sky did they have? What sort of Baustelle? What did their Jew-Chief look like? How many portions were cut there from one loaf—

"Load the shit up!"

Suddenly all the corpses in the Carrion Shed became alike in his eyes. Before, he had wanted to see Zanvil Lubliner off for the last time. Now he grabs them and drags them as they come: when the SS driver gets back, they all have to be loaded up on the van. Pini, Red Itche-Meyer's son, couldn't have been as heavy alive as he is now. How is it they left the trousers on him? Short trousers, but they still look like something. Pini's bare feet trail along the ground. Such long legs. Never showed on Pini that his legs are so long. Oh, the seat of his trousers is in shreds. No wonder they left them on him.

"Students like Pini are the pride and glory of the Sages of Lublin Yeshiva," Rabbi Shapiro, its founder and dean, had said. And Pini really was a prodigy.

Now his bare feet drag clumsily in the dust of the parade ground, as if he were stubbornly refusing to get on the van. When Spitz, the Jew-Chief, was about to let his father have "twenty in the arse," Pini hurled himself on the flogging bench and cried and begged, "Dear Jew-Chief! Sweet Jew-Chief! Kill me instead of papa!" Now you have all you can do to get him on the van.

Strange thing about the camp. The weak often hold out longer than the sturdy. Fifty-year-old Itche-Meyer, that withered stalk, is still around. Young Pini died a Mussulman, while his tottering father still goes out to the Baustelle every day. Where does such a man get his strength? He's always shut up within himself, as in a suit of armour—silent. But his silence isn't the silence of a Mussulman. His eyes aren't calcified—and the eyes are the main thing. Everything is mirrored in the eyes, from the first hint of Mussulmanishness to the oncoming end. THE EYES. The well-known Mussulman eyes. The X-ray of the Campling. First they mirror the calcifying soul, only then the calcified body. Where, then, are Itche-Meyer's fiery eyes constantly gazing?

The day Pini died, Itche-Meyer refused to say Kaddish[1] for him. "Pini is alive!" he said. "You don't say Kaddish for Prophet Elijah[2] ... Pini is alive! Pini has gone right to Heaven like a Seraph. Pini never even had a taste of sin." After the first gong that night, he stole off to the Carrion Shed and there sat up with Pini in the dark all night. But in the morning, before the march to the Baustelle, Itche-Meyer got together a Minyan[3] under Pini's bunk and recited Kaddish for his son. What happened to Red Itche-Meyer during the night in the Carrion Shed? Was it revealed to him that Pini's body hadn't been smelted and refined enough

[1] Kaddish: Jewish prayer for the dead said by mourners.

[2] According to the Bible, the prophet Elijah did not die, but went up to heaven in a fiery chariot.

[3] Minyan: quorum of ten adult male Jews traditionally required for the full prayer service.

to make him worthy of going to Heaven as a flaming Seraph? Or did he, in the course of the night, discover a blemish in his own soul, that is: who and what does he think he is that he should dare rule upon such mysteries? While he was reciting the Kaddish the gong tolled. All the others dashed out to roll call, but the ten stood quaking, one foot with Itche-Meyer and the other reaching desperately for the parade ground. They waited with taut, quivering breath to hear Itche-Meyer end the Kaddish so they could let out the final "Amen" and make for the parade ground.

The van opening was too high. The sweat ran in rivulets off his face. He felt his strength draining from him. He barely managed to throw the upper half of Pini's body on the tail-board. He pulled himself up on to the van and began dragging Pini inside.

"Pini has gone to Heaven like a Seraph . . ."

Behind Harry's back lay the stack of arms and legs of Mussulman-skeletons. He dragged Pini to the bone heap. The van still had to collect much "shit" from many camps today. He placed Pini at the foot of the heap. In the world of human beings death is uniform while life varies. Just the opposite in camp—one life and an assortment of deaths. Pini there, he looks altogether different from those on the stack. Not just him, all the bodies from the Carrion Shed look completely different from those. And the others to be loaded here today will probably look still different. Camp by camp will be stacked here, each as a separate race; like various specimens of different planets. Alive, they were all alike. The camps are all as identical to each other as drops in the same bloodstream. *"Students like Pini are the pride and glory of the Sages of Lublin Yeshiva . . ."* Maybe there, in the stack, lies another, similar prodigy from the Sages of Lublin. Why do they look so different, now? Why don't they give one another any signs of recognition? Maybe they used to sit on the same bench at the Yeshiva, shoulder to shoulder. Why doesn't any of it show on them now? Maybe at a third camp they'll load on another school-brother of theirs. Then why don't they identify themselves to one another? Here, in the van, there are none of the barriers that had separated and segregated them from each other in the camps. Here they're together again. It may happen that here, within the stack, school-brother's arm bones will again join brother's, as in old times, in a New Month Feast roundelay at the Sages of

Lublin. Then why do they ignore each other? Why don't they recognize one another any more?

"*Load the shit up! . . .*"

. . . The SS driver will soon be out, and he's standing around here musing like a philosopher. He placed Pini at the base of the stack and let himself down from the van to go on with the loading.

. . . What's this truck now pulling into camp? A new SS guard unit? This is the third time since he's been here that the guard has been changed. And the replacements are always worse. That looks like the German blonde getting off.

Looking into the darkness of the van from this far, Pini seems like a potato that has rolled off a potato pile; as though they had deliberately thrown him off themselves: they don't want any strangers mingling with them. They have a secret all their own, not meant for others to hear. Each camp has its private secret—the secret which closed them in like walls of a pot and cooked them together. What trace, then, could have remained of their previous lives? Everything was burned through and through. Now they have their special shared secret; they stem from a common pot. Funny thing: young Pini is already lying in the van, and his fifty-year-old father—he's still out at the Baustelle, shovel in hand. Sooner or later the Cat will mark him down in the book again. Itche-Meyer's ruddy scalp glitters like copper under the Baustelle sky. Queer colour of skull. Eye-catching.

He drags them all from the Carrion Shed. But he by-passes Zanvil Lubliner, as if ignoring him. As if feeling that by throwing him into the van he'll be killing him with his own hands. Toward the end Zanvil had stopped coming to the sick bay. The last time, he showed up with a strange request:

"Preleshnik, it's too bad, the helpings you give me every day. I haven't much more suffering to go, anyway. Better to give them to some younger ones. Just one thing: when you get out of here, be so good as to go to my wife and children and tell them I was accidentally killed by a locomotive during work. I wouldn't like them to know I rotted away like this . . ."

In Schwecher's tailor shop, Zanvil was the master tailor. He set the pace and his word went. He had strong, brawny arms, a sturdy body, and warm, tender eyes. All the grief of the ghetto was reflected in those eyes. He could finish off the buttonholes for 175 Luftwaffe jackets in half a work-shift. But Zanvil was always the last to finish. So long as a single tailor was still sweating at the buttonhole machine, Zanvil didn't get up from his work. Poldek, the shop super-visor, always checked how far Zanvil was along in his work: if Zanvil hasn't completed the quota, there's no use raising it. Whom didn't Zanvil Lubliner help! And how many Jews did he save from Poldek this way! Who else used to cheer up and encourage everyone at the shop? No sooner did Poldek step out than Zanvil's voice would ring through the shop:

"Jews! Sew them their shrouds! We'll outlive them, may they fry in hell!"

Now he lies on the ground of the Carrion Shed, looking like a puny, dead embryo. So tiny, so shrivelled. Not a stitch worth stealing left on him. Toward the end, he had been going out to the Baustelle barefooted. If he'd given Zanvil his shoes, he might still be alive. The first sign of the soul Mussulmanized is going about the camp barefooted. But the Camp Commander would have a fit if he saw his "physician" going around in bare feet. He—the "physician" —doesn't belong to himself. *He* is an item in the sick-bay inventory, an indispensable part of it. Like the white-lacquered crib; like an empty medicine bottle; like an empty box of pills which mustn't be thrown away. The "physician" doesn't belong to himself. True, no one here belongs to himself, but it must be remembered that the sick bay is the Camp Commander's pet plaything. No doubt that Zanvil would still be alive if he'd had shoes on his feet. Many of them would still be alive if they had been allowed to lie, even one single day, in the sick bay. What's the use of the crib? What use are shoes to him as a "physician" who does nothing but dawdle about the camp? *"I wouldn't like my wife and children to know I rotted away like this."* Can this thing lying here on the ground once have been Zanvil Lubliner—

"How's it coming, Medic?"

The SS driver came out of the German Quarters, face florid, eyes drunk, black SS cap perched back on his pate. He buckled the military belt on his black tunic as he ran his eyes over the opening into the van.

"What slop!" he growled. "That's no order. That's a shit pile!"

The SS man climbed into the van. He didn't at all care for the arrangement inside. One after the other he snatched up the Carrion Shed corpses and flung them on to the bone stack. Those hurled didn't roll off. The stack didn't totter a bit. Not at all like a potato pile. Pini's trousers showed like a dark blotch on the bone stack. His trousers were still visible, but he himself was immediately sucked into the pile. He was no longer to be seen.

From opposite the opening the stack looked as before, as if not a skeleton had been added to it, as though it hadn't sucked in every last Carrion Shed skeleton. They vanished into the pile as though they had never existed, only the blotch that was Pini's trousers showing on the skeleton stack like an eccentric patch, refusing to be assimilated into the chalkiness of the bones. The van again looked like a tidy, clean-swept, empty house. Much "shit" from many camps still had to be loaded today.

The SS driver hopped down from the van, raised the tailboard, and slammed it shut. Job's done.

"One more corpse in the Carrion Shed," Harry said.

Fire showered from his eyes. He felt the hard earth of the parade ground under his arms. He rolled over several times. He couldn't get up from the impact of the blow smashed into his face.

"Pusbag!" the German snarled. "Stinking pusbag!"

The SS driver went into the shed, grabbed the man by the foot and dragged him to the van. The punch jangled like heavy bells around his head, but he felt no pain. Zanvil Lubliner's head trailed on the ground behind the German's feet like the dangling head of a slaughtered fowl. *"I wouldn't like my wife and children to know I rotted away like this."* The ear that took the blow was deafened, but it was with this ear that he now distinctly heard the pleading voice of Zanvil Lubliner.

The German picked up Zanvil Lubliner like a dried rabbit skin. He hurled him deep into the van, slammed the tailboard shut, and hopped into the cab. The motor coughed, started up. The van turned toward the camp gate, went out to the road. The dust swirled among the barbed wires like white smoke of a fire. All around an emptiness flowed and spread. But in Harry's ears the ignited motor still spluttered:

Pusbag. Pusbag. Pusbag . . .

Harry struggled to get up from the ground. He felt his strength oozing from him like last drops from a drained glass. He barely dragged himself to the block gate.

II

It was dark in the block. He stepped heavily between the bunks toward the sick bay. Behind him, day peered in through the open block gate as into a dark, full van. The three-tiered hutches filled the block to the rafters. It looked like a tall stack of dead Mussulmen. A full van. The blow smarted on his face and he just couldn't make out which of his two ears was deafened. The block was full beyond measure and the fullness jammed into his ears. On the other side of the wooden kitchen partition the Germans were having a drunken orgy. Their revelry carried through the wooden partition. He was walking in the block as inside a travelling sealed van crammed with bones of dead Mussulmen.

In the sick bay, on the table, the necks of the empty bottles stood in three straight rows, one beside the other, mute and impassive. Their muteness amplified the dull roar in his ears. He could no longer bear the order, the compactness on the table. He could feel the compactness cramping his brain. The white sheet was spread on the white-lacquered crib—taut, smooth, without the slightest wrinkle. Not a prisoner had ever lain on this bed. The whiteness of the sheet splashed against his eyes like a white puddle; a blood puddle not red but white. The puddle floated over the walls and around the corners. From the glass cabinet his bread ration looked out to him—whole, untouched—against a background of tall white cartons and flat aluminium boxes, all in precise formation by height. He didn't feel any hunger. He returned the bread an indifferent look. It didn't cheer him up this time. He wouldn't care if someone stole it from him. He wouldn't miss it. This evening he'll be getting another ration. Two portions of bread! He started up from the chair. The last thought stuck in his mind: *two portions of bread?* He's never yet had two portions of bread here. Under the armpits of dead Mussulmen they often find two portions of bread... A shudder ran through him. His body shook all over. TWO PORTIONS OF BREAD. All at once, he felt that the heart

204

inside him had eyes. Enormous eyes. And huge tears were dropping from those eyes: *he—he is going to have TWO portions of bread . . .*

Through the glass of the medicine cabinet the black piece of bread was looking out at him. *I'm sick!* he thought. The bread lay aloof, distant; his, yet not his; stripped of the rapture which such a bread ration should arouse in a campling—dead stuff. Just bread.

Above all watch out not to become spiritual Mussulmen. Hold tight. Don't resign yourselves. Don't give up. Then your bodies will hold out longer and you won't become physical Mussulmen. This is the way he sermonizes to the prisoners day in day out. He, sitting all day in the shelter of the sick bay, doing nothing, not getting flogged; he, who gets a double helping of soup—for him it's easy to preach: *Hold tight. Don't give up.* But isn't he now about to become a spiritual Mussulman?

The sick-bay door stood open.

His brain was reeling. He felt as if he were drifting through waves of murk. His strength is leaving him and the shore moves further and further away. *Hold tight! Don't give up!* Who's going to help him here? He's going under. The shoreline recedes, melts to a grey fog. Who's going to come to his help? *Spiritual Mussulman. Spiritual Mussulman.* On the site of the bed there was now just a blob of white. The blob floated around the sick bay, swelled and burst, its white shreds hanging down from the dark corners. He couldn't bear it any more. He groped toward the door, fumbled for the exit. He felt himself drifting under the murky waves.

From the distance, day peered in through the block gate as into the dark of a sealed van. *"Such slop!"* Here, in the narrow aisle between the triple-deck hutches, there's still enough room for plenty of Mussulmen. The SS driver would have crushed him into the ground if hě'd noticed. All that space going to waste. So much "shit" from so many camps can still be loaded here. But it's not his fault. Right here Red Itche-Meyer stood this morning with ten prisoners around him, saying the first Kaddish for Pini. Why doesn't he miss Zanvil Lubliner at all? One after the other they're carting them away—old acquaintances and new, friends of long ago and new friends. They never come back. Suddenly they drop out of sight, and you never see them again. Still, you just don't miss them. They're wiped away like the writing on a magic slate when the carbon sheet is pulled up. You don't see those who've gone, but those who are left. As though it is not the gone who have died, but the remaining. And you can't mourn the death of those who have gone while you're looking on at the death of those left, those still hanging around the camp. Why doesn't he feel Zanvil's absence? Zanvil won't be coming back from the Baustelle any more with grimy bare feet running blood and pus. He'll never again come into the sick bay, and he, Harry, won't ever find him in his hutch any more. Zanvil, his teacher at Schwecher's tailor shop, who taught him how to fix the buttonhole machine when it stuck; Zanvil, who never got tired of showing him over and over again how to feed the Luftwaffe tunic into the machine so that the needle shouldn't jump into his finger and the German supervisor see that he, Harry, wasn't a craftsman but a faker—Zanvil is no more. He won't even be able to repay him any more for all he had done for him. Why doesn't he miss him? As if Zanvil Lubliner isn't gone at all but is lying here in the block on the pile of Mussulmen. The block—like a packed van—rides out of camp. And Harry rides along. He and Zanvil are staying together.

"Preleshnik, when you get out of here."

Get out of here how? Get out where? What does this "out" look like? The block is riding like a sealed SS van. Everyone is being taken away. He too. Where? He's been thrown into the van on the stack of wooden hutches. Bones. Bones. Where are they being taken? How many more times will they be taken like this? Where's the van heading for now? Can this really be the last time they're being taken? At every roundup in the ghetto he would think: this is the last time! ... When he was deported from the ghetto he was sure: *this* must be the last time! ... When the "Lame Slavedealer" picked him out of the ranks at Camp Sakrau he knew that this *must* be the last time! Where's he being taken now? How many such "last times" are there? Where is the van taking the bones? At what kind of place will it pull in? *Then* where will they be taken from there, from that mysterious place? Always taken to a mysterious place, and always taken from that mysterious place to another mysterious place. Always taken. Always tossed into big, dark vans. Always bones stacked on bones. Sometimes live bones,

206

sometimes dead bones. It's all the same. They live afterwards just the way they lived before; and they're tossed into the van before just as they're tossed into it afterwards; and always, both in the "before" and in the "afterwards," the bones think the same thoughts.

Here, right on this spot, the Minyan stood this morning. This morning—like all the rest of the mornings—was all bedlam. The blockful of bones clacked against each other, rackety as a wagonload of scrap iron. Who will say Kaddish for Itche-Meyer? If the Cat marks him down in the memo book today, will Pini hop off the bone heap to throw himself on the bench, or will the bench wait, empty, for Itche-Meyer to come and lie down on it himself? The Cat won't make any more memos on Zanvil. And maybe? Maybe there, at the van's last stop, there is another such Cat, who will again make memos on Zanvil? No matter where they take you— there's such a Cat. No matter where, there are Germans. Bones and Germans. Heaven must also be full of Germans. Bones and Germans.

Whenever ten men are needed for a Minyan, they run first for the medic. Medic, they figure, always has time. He won't turn them down though he doesn't go for all that himself. It was Zanvil who got it going. Probably won't be any more praying here. And Zanvil won't be getting up the Sabbath-morning Minyan any more. This morning, Itche-Meyer just couldn't get his mouth to let go the words of Kaddish:

"Yisgadal veyiskadash . . .[1] Oh, Pini—Pini—"

Everyone rushed out for roll call. The gong was ringing. The "ten" were beside themselves, desperate to dash out to roll call. And Itche-Meyer—still at it, "*Yisgadal veyiskadash . . .* Oh, Pini—Pini—"

The ten finally bolted out. He tailed after them, got into the ranks, marched out to the Baustelle—all the while his lips muttering: "*Yisgadal veyiskadash . . .* Pini—Pini—"

Why don't they take everyone away together? When Red Itche-Meyer gets back from the Baustelle, the Carrion Shed will already be empty. The Jew-Chief will probably put on the white smock—and take over as medic. The Camp Commander won't have his sick bay without a "physician." Everyone will be swept away from here, except the bottles on

[1] Opening words of Kaddish.

the sick-bay table. How long since Zanvil Lubliner was still Zanvil Lubliner? It was only two or three days ago that he stopped feeling hungry, gazed at the block like a "philosopher," lay down and waited to be carried out to the Carrion Shed. A Mussulman never closes his eyes. Once he starts gazing with them like a "philosopher"—he never stops gazing that way. When does a Mussulman die? Spitz let Zanvil have it with an iron wire across the face to get him up and out for roll call. He didn't believe him that he was really dead. "Let the medic come and settle if it's a stiff laying on the bunk or a bloody loafer." Spitz will put on the white smock, stand arms akimbo—like Siegfried, the SS man, when he's about to pound the life out of a prisoner—and feel himself ruler of the roost. When does a Mussulman die? Is it only when he's tossed into the van, or when he's still mooning around the camp, a "philosopher"? Or maybe the Mussulman doesn't die at all—for the dead can't die. Maybe he himself is long since dead and is only roaming around here a Mussulman among Mussulmen. In the evening the block orderlies will be back from the Baustelle. They'll drag him out and throw him into the Carrion Shed. Spitz will eat up the bread ration in the medicine cabinet. Too bad about that piece of bread. Better architect Weisblum should have it. Who'll tell him to get it there? If he tells the block orderlies while they're carrying him, they'll just keep the bread for themselves. He won't be much of a scare to them now: they're taking him to the Carrion Shed. The block orderlies are a vicious crew. In all the camps the block orderlies are rotten, low-down creatures, without heart or conscience. How they fawned on him and played up to him when he was medic. Architect Weisblum will probably never become a Mussulman. Nonsense! That's what he thought about Zanvil Lubliner. Look where it left him in the end. God, if only that racket in the head would let up a bit! Must be that all Mussulmen hear this sort of dull roar in the ears. That's why they don't hear when they're being spoken to. Just stare blankly, blankly . . .

The kitchen door was open. Eyes of Mussulmen stare blankly . . . The German blonde comes closer, reeling toward him. Her eyes hang on to his. Her gait—like the SS driver's—drunken. In the narrow aisle between the three-tier hutches her nude shoulders arch white, like a slope of the mound of Mussulmen in the van. The trousers! Where

208

are Pini's trousers? He stood staring blankly ahead. Just the way the SS driver came at him before. He didn't budge: *Pusbag. Pusbag. Pusbag . . .*

He stood there, staring. All Mussulmen stand and stare this way. Don't run away. He's never seen a Mussulman run. The Mussulman stands, stares, and stares blankly . . .

She wrapped her arms around him. She was at his feet, stretching out nude arms to him. She was stroking the skirt of his white smock:

"Oh, Holy One . . ."

Over against his eyes the kitchen door stood open. He saw: a half-window. A normal window. A light-letting window. A window of another world. A barless window—the way windows used to be. A window set with panes—faces of daylight. A white-lacquered sill. Loaves of bread on the sill, one on top of the other, small, oblong loaves—whole. He'd already forgotten what a whole bread looks like. At camp you see only ration slices.

"Oh, Holy one! Look at me," she blubbered.

It was as in a dream. He heard the voice as through thick walls, as with clogged ears, as though he were under water. Like one nailed to a cross he stood riveted to the air behind him. He couldn't move and didn't have the strength even to try. His will was clotted as his whole being was clotted. He didn't scare and he didn't draw back. His fear was calcified, sucked dry. A weird, novel fear. A fear sapped of the liquid venom, as though the warm torso of a serpent were wrapped around him, with two teats instead of fangs bared at him.

It was as in a dream. A static, immobile dream filled with emptiness. Like a bayoneted rifle aimed upward, not at the heart.

Siegfried the SS man appeared in the kitchen doorway. His hulk blocked the half-window and the whole loaves of bread on the sill. Harry felt no fear, since everything was devoid of reality, as in a stupor. He wanted to wonder: why didn't he feel any fear? But he didn't wonder. It was good to feel this way. It was good to feel no fear. As though Siegfried no longer had the power to harm him. No one could harm him any more. He felt he had just crossed a boundary. There was a boundary, and he had crossed it. Crossed—but not far over. He is still able to look back to the side he came from, and he can see everything, everything, just as if he were still there.

Siegfried stands without his black tunic, arms akimbo. Queer. In his white undershirt, Siegfried is more terrifying than in his black SS tunic. The German woman is kneeling at his feet. He hears and doesn't hear. They're talking to each other—she to Siegfried and Siegfried to her. What's there to talk about him? What's there to talk about a prisoner who is about to be tossed on the van? It's him they're talking about. He hears. He sees. He stares, the way the three-tier hutches stare, the way the skeleton skulls in the van stare.

"Please take him along there," the German woman pleads drunkenly. "I'll do anything you want, Siegfried."

In Siegfried's belt buckle an eagle spreads its wings above a swastika. Just like the Gestapo seal on the labour card at Schwecher's shop. The arms of the swastika terrify him more than the clenched fists on Siegfried's hips. A cold shiver runs over him. *The arms of the swastika . . .*

"Come on, Medic!"

Siegfried pulls him. The triple-deck hutches move backward. He walks, but he feels that he is standing. The German woman pushes him from behind and whimpers drunkenly. Zanvil Lubliner's head is trailing behind the SS driver like the dangling head of a slaughtered fowl, but he clearly sees that it isn't Zanvil's head but his own. *The arms of the swastika.* The first time he saw them was the morning the Germans came into Metropoli. They herded all the Jews into the workrooms of the Gutstein Brothers' plant. They called them to the table, one at a time. The arms of the swastika sprawled across a red flag—a giant crab weltering in blood.

"What is Hitler?" the Germans asked.

The blood gushed from the mangled body of the Jew. The arms of the swastika whirl on the red German flag like the blades of an enormous meat chopper.

"What is Hitler?"

She caresses him: "Oh, Holy One!" and whimpers into his ear, drunk, half-naked.

The air coagulated around him and he was clotted into it. The bunks have vanished like the departed van. Where the van had stood there remained only gnawing, aching daylight. The kitchen doorway engulfs him like the light of the parade ground cleared of the van. The old Volksdeutsche cook

210

stands facing the stove, sleeves rolled up her arms. Gusts of vapour spurt from the cauldrons. Today it's probably jacket potatoes. What's Spitz's flogging bench doing there? Siegfried drags him. Hitler gapes down wild-eyed from the kitchen wall: what's a Jew doing in the German kitchen? Kill! Kill! Kill! ... "Oh, Holy One!" the drunken German woman whimpers, opening the second kitchen door. The cook goes on standing over the steaming cauldrons; doesn't even look up. As though nothing unusual were happening in the kitchen. Moment links with moment. A steel chain. No gap. An onrushing cataract. Drop dissolves in drop. Infinity and split second melt into one. Beginning and end converge. It's a mute life-and-death puppet show; someone commands your moves; someone pulls you by the sleeve; speech. But the life around you is inarticulate, unreal.

Air of the German pale. Here, here is their sphere. Here they live. This is the way to the German Quarters. A passage-way. A stair vestibule. Clean, sharp, cool as the blade of a slaughter knife.

He's long since forgotten that in the world, once, there were stairs, a wooden banister, knobs and doors behind which a person could lock himself in and have solitude. Lock himself in—and still be free. He's long since forgotten, though in that world he himself had gone up and down such stairs, gone in and out of the door—whenever he felt like it. Not led. Not dragged. There, every door had—a marker. Even the door of his house had a marker. A bronze marker, with his name engraved on it—oh yes, he had had a name. A name all his own. A personal, private name. Everybody was a somebody, then, and he was also—somebody. Once it was "stair-vestibule." Just that—STAIR VESTIBULE. Now—it's SS! The stairs—SS-ish. As if the stairs were out-fitted in a black SS tunic; the banister grillework, with a swastika in the centre. Stairs—not on which you walk, but which walk you, lead you like SS men. Where are the stairs taking you? Where does the van go when it leaves the camp? At what kind of place will the van pull up? What kind of place is he being taken to now? Again they're leading him. How many times more will he be led like this? What's at the place he's being led to?

The sensation of roundup in the ghetto came over him; the feeling of Selektion during a German Aktion in the ghetto—

How many times does a man die?

211

III

He was standing inside, by the door, as on the threshold between dreaming nightmare and waking to madness. The German Quarters! He's inside. He could tangibly feel the thoughts churning and somersaulting in his mind. The scene clawed into his brain and turned his mind topsy-turvy. Like someone standing on his head for the first time, seeing houses growing down from above, roofs reaching down into the sky. He can't be here—but here he is. His eyes plainly see it. Here they are, the wild drunken voices. Back there in the sick bay he heard them. Now—he sees them. Sprawling mouths. He doesn't hear the shouts, he sees them. They're closing in on him. He's standing amid them, sinking, sinking into them. He can no longer find himself. Can't feel himself. In the hanging yellow of the air only the whiteness of his smock reminds him that he's here in a real body. And as he remembers, his subconscious feels in a spasm the full horror of it: *the voices of the German Quarters.* Oh ... oh ... he must hurry and rush up and hide in the dark in a hutch on the third tier. At Camp Sakrau the Germans got hold of the Jew-Chief and hauled him into their Quarters. When the prisoners came back from the Baustelle they found him lying in one of the blocks—dead, naked, his body a mess of queer blue spots. What's he doing here? How did he get here?

It's: shrieking bedlam. It's: brain inside out. It's: deaf blankness. No one pays attention to him here. The German woman is still kneeling at his feet. The bedlam drowns out her bleating. On the windows the sun sprawls behind lowered yellow shades. Everything is soggy with thick yellow light. Bottles—empty, part empty, overturned and scattered—rolling on the floor among wriggling naked bodies of men and women moaning and panting drunkenly. No one pays attention to him here. No one notices him. No one wonders: what's the medic doing here in his white smock? Everything swarms, wriggles, yet is frozen still as the heavy yellow light. Everything is normal here. The wildest absurdity—the soberest reality. Anything passes here, anything is possible, the way anything passes and is possible in insanity. Death and life dwell together here. Blood and wine are drunk from the same flasks. The Carrion Shed and the SS rooms are one. Borders erased. Boundaries lost. Below—the prisoners' block; above—the SS rooms. The prisoners' block—like a wine cellar beneath the German Quarters. Each made for the other. Each fulfilling the other. Cellar and salon meet here like wine flasks on the tables of the rich.

The Cat is holding a woman on his knees. He moans and wails into her. His gaping mouth is like a dark toothless cavern. His eyes squint as in pain. His black whisker ends tailing down the sides of his mouth dilate the blackness of his cave mouth. He kneads and pinches the woman's naked flesh with his fingers, letting out odd mewls.

The Cat . . .

The Cat is off duty from the Baustelle today. Today his memo book won't be operating. The flogging bench stands idle in the kitchen. What's the bench doing in the kitchen? The Cat wants to sink his gaping mouth into the woman's flesh, but he has no teeth. And with screwed-up eyes he looses heart-rending caterwauls up into the thick yellow air.

What's he doing here in the German Quarters? How did he get here? No one wonders about it. As though his standing here were a normal, perfectly reasonable fact. Here everything is reasonable. Here there are no qualms, no doubts. Here it's chaos; a yellow hodge-podge of nudity and bottles on the floor. "*Siegfried, please take him along.*" It's a bacchanalia of sound which is ear-splitting stillness; weeping which is laughter. The young Jew-Chief at Sakrau was thrown into the block—dead, queer blue spots on his body. What did they do to him? What will Siegfried do to him now? How did he get here? The four legs of the overturned table jut up into the yellow air. Bottles and nudity. He can't remember. He seeks but just cannot find himself. *The German Quarters!* What will happen to him here? The German woman is pouring it down her mouth from a full bottle. She's sprawled on the floor in front of him, struggling to get up, to kneel at his feet again. But she can't. "*Come on, Medic.*" Siegfried then went into the next room. He'll probably be right out. Hitler looks in through the open door from the wall of the next room. A brown cape on his shoulders. Thunderheads pile up behind him. The picture is fire-red and brown. As though he were soaring through a tempest of flame. The arms of the swastika on Hitler's armband grow huger, huger. The band is red. Everything turns red. A sea of flaming red. And in the centre, the arms of the swastika twirl like the blades of a windmill "*What is Hitler?*" Soon the Germans will summon him to the judgment table in the workrooms of the Gutstein Brothers' plant. He is down on his knees together with all the Metropoli Jews. Any moment now they'll call him out of the kneeling mass. They'll ask him, "*What is Hitler?*"

Out of a corner emerges a nude woman. She moves like a sleepwalker. The window blinds shut out the sun like a beast blocking off the light with its glossy yellow pelt. Everything is drenched with yellow. What's that?—what's that scratching between the woman's breasts? The letters tumble about before his eyes. He can in no way put them together. The digits beneath them leap up among the letters and jumble up with them. The German woman is still trying to wrap her arms around his legs, snorting drunkenly. The upturned table legs twirl before his eyes like the arms of the swastika on a yellow armband. The blue eyes of the woman hook into his brain. How did these eyes get here? Where did they suddenly float up from? What are Daniella's blue eyes doing here? "*The loveliest couple in the world, Papa and Mama.*" Dani's voice... The eyes scream... Her mouth gapes... It's Daniella's voice screaming to him. He hears. He clearly hears.

"HARRY!!! HARRY!!!"

IV

He was lying on the floor outside, by the stairs. When he opened his eyes the two black boots of the Camp Commander were standing beside his head. Stillness sprang upon him as if thousands of motors had suddenly stopped roaring in his ears. The sudden braking of the din was more deafening than the din itself. He could feel the stillness stream into him. The shouts of the Germans now reached him from behind the closed doors more muffled than he used to hear them in the sick bay. The Camp Commander's face was grave, meditative: should he finish him off? Should he crush him with his boot and have done with the shit? Or should he let him live and continue as physician?

He was lying on the floor by the stairs and he felt that his life now lay on the floor beside him like a severed object.

Any moment and the black boot would trample it. He couldn't move. He was unable to breathe, to disgorge from inside him either plea or anger, pain or vengeance. He lay as if bound to a sacrificial altar. He raised his eyelids, looked upward, saw as through a fine-spun veil: now everything is transparent, now it's all blurred. Now he sees, hears, understands and knows everything that happened to him, and now he knows nothing at all. Is his life still alive, or has it already been crushed? He's right here, and he isn't here. Here are the high black boot tops; the Camp Commander's face; the walls of the stair-vestibule; doors—he sees them all. And now everything is again swamped with yellow chaos. Eyes—blue eyes, wide open in scream: *Harry! Harry!* And again —stillness. As if the roar of thousands of motors had suddenly stopped in his ears. Stillness . . .

Beside him on the floor lies his life like an infant of his. Any moment now the black boot will crush it, and it won't show any more from under the boot sole. Any second now. The infant lies beside him . . .

He's lying on the floor. The black sheen of the boots gleams by his head. He lifts his eyes, looks upward: *the Camp Commander's eyes* . . .

The face above folded into a smile. The boots turned and walked to the door. The Commander opened the door, walked in, shut it. Stillness. He's lying on the floor. Opposite him lies his life, way off from him.

Waves upon waves. The walls of the stair-vestibule toss on a high sea. Yellow. Red. Waves toss him between open doors, and the swastika on Siegfried's belt buckle looms up between the waves.

"Take him back where you brought him from!" the Commander orders.

Siegfried is dragging him over the stairs, but he doesn't feel himself being dragged. Pini's bare feet trail across the parade ground, still stubbornly refusing to get up on the van.

The cook, the old Volksdeutsche, is still standing at the stove. Sleeves rolled up, she goes on stirring in the cauldrons and doesn't turn her head. As though it were a natural thing, his being dragged back along the kitchen floor now. Normal —as the potatoes she is now boiling in the cauldrons; as the small black breads lying there on the window sill, each of which she will cut up into twelve rations. Normal—as everything around here is normal: the prisoners' block on that side of the kitchen and the German Quarters on this; the sky showing through the window; Hitler's picture on the kitchen wall.

Columns of steam erupt from the cauldrons, and the old cook doesn't even turn her head.

Two rows of triple-deck hutches join him, drag along with him through the darkness of the block. Where's he being dragged? Where will they halt? He suddenly feels a sharp pain ram into his ribs. The pain leaps up into his throat and plugs his breath.

Siegfried has paid the medic back with a fist in the ribs and a boot in the belly for having had to carry him. He was boiling mad: Since when has Siegfried got to carry a living Jew?

He dumped him on the ground, spat disgustedly, and was gone.

Pain crouched around him, looking him straight in the eyes, stalking him like a pack of trained SS hounds. With the least stir of a limb the pain pounced upon him and drove sharp fangs deep, deep into him. He was lying on the ground and he couldn't, he didn't dare so much as raise his head.

He was lying face down. All around, everything was dead, empty. The ground was close by his eyes—unyielding, unpitying. He could see the ground, but couldn't flee into it. It was shut beneath him like the locked door of someone else's bunker during a German Aktion in the ghetto. He felt he was on the outside.

The hutches towered vacant over him. When the prisoners get back from the Baustelle they'll find him lying on the ground of the block. The Jew-Chief at Sakrau lay nude, with queer spots all over his body. Is he also lying nude now, or is he still in his white smock? Spitz will order two block orderlies to carry him over to the Carrion Shed. The ten Jews bolt out to roll call. Red Itche-Meyer weeping: *"Yisgadal veyiskadash . . ."* And Dani's voice screaming to him: *"Harry!!! Harry!!!"* Turmoil. He must be out of his mind! But he did see and hear! But where did Dani come here from? But he plainly saw Daniella's eyes! He's out of his mind! But he did hear her cry: *"Harry!"* The screams are still ringing in his ears. What happened to him next? Where is he now? The van pulled up at the Carrion Shed. He clearly remembers that. He was waiting for the van, waiting to see Zanvil Lubliner off. He remembers it exactly.

216

He can still hear the rumble of the approaching van. No. He didn't dream it. Then he was dragging the corpses. He climbed into the van. He lay down and sank in among the dead Mussulmen. He was riding. He clearly remembers feeling that the van was riding, and that he was riding in it.

Where are they all? As soon as he gets out he must first go to Zanvil Lubliner's wife and children and tell them their father didn't rot away like a stinking Mussulman. That's a sacred vow! *Pusbag. Pusbag. Pusbag.* What happened to him next? Where did the van take him? Where did he come across Daniella's eyes?

The Camp Commander was bending over him. He took him up in his arms and carried him into the sick bay.

He was lying on the white sheet in the white-lacquered crib —no, no! That's prohibited! Strictly prohibited! The Camp Commander's face smiled forgiveness at him. The Commander pulled out his cigarette case. A white "R.6" cylinder tumbled down and rolled away from the black boots. The Commander lit himself a cigarette, and the black sheen of his boots was gone beyond the sick-bay door.

On the table, the medicine bottles stood in three straight rows, like prisoners at roll call. From the small glass cabinet on the wall there stared at him—whole, untouched—the bread ration. By the table, opposite each other, stood two chairs: one for the medic, one for the Mussulman. The chairs were empty.

Suddenly, he felt an awful pain around his eyes. From every limb of his body, from his skin, from the roots of his hair, the pain converged upon his eyes and all started beseeching him:

"A tear—a tear—please, just one . . ."

He rolled off the white sheet. The searing pain around the eyes grew more agonizing, more excruciating. A roaring blaze. The pupils of his eyes flared up like two seething volcanoes, and the pain erupted and streamed into his every bone. He dragged himself to the table, let himself into the Mussulman seat. Queer sounds started escaping from his throat. The weird cheeping of an ailing bird. His arms reached out to the empty chair opposite.

"A tear—please, only one—just one . . ."

He lifted his gnarled, calcified hands and pointed to his eyelids: There . . . he . . . he feels something there, some-

217

thing he's never felt before ... He twittered and breathed his plea to the empty chair:

"... Tear ... only ... only one ..."

Hippocrates of Concentration Camp Universe! Prescribe this patient his cure!

19

FELLA was pressing Daniella's shoulders to the latrine wall with all her might, as though she were grappling with some-one out to harm her.

She felt she had control of the body clamped between her hands, but not of the mad demon thrashing about and struggling inside this body. Daniella's head strained violently, unremittingly to break through the half-open latrine gate out to the night—to death.

No use wasting words. No use trying to convince. Some-thing horrible is about to happen. She forces Daniella back against the wall, keeping between her and the gate. She keeps a tight grip on the body—but this isn't Daniella. A fiend has got into her, and it's the fiend now fighting to break loose. It she can't check. It she is powerless to overcome.

Beyond the bridge, above the treetops, a profile moon hurries across the sky as though on an important and urgent mission. The moon looks like a jester—fool's cap on head, pointed beard on chin. Tatters of clouds, like gauzy white veils, clutter its way, but it cuts through them and hurries on —yet remains at a standstill, over the Execution Square.

They were by the half-open latrine gate. To the right, opposite the KB, the round lake lay on the ground like a head flung into the Joy Division, the wooden bridge like a noose around its neck. Daniella's eyes blazed with uncanny light and her lips moved:

"HARRY'S STANDING IN A WHITE CLOUD ..."

The red bulbs above the electric barbed wire looked at the Joy Division like glowering eyes guarding the rosy blocks. Opposite, the night dipped nude in the lake by the light of the red bulbs. The forward end of the bridge was a haze of crimson. Nearby, from the sealed end of the KB block a weird cooing rose as from a dovecote—a kind of madman's lament. Mid-lake, where red verged on black, the brace of swans stood white, like two marble statues in reverie, gazing at the Joy Division. The KB was steeped in darkness. The mournful plaint rose from the block, as if the souls of the departed girls had come back to bewail in the dead of night those not yet gone.

Daniella's eyes ploughed toward the lake: the sentry booth on the bridge is set back in the dark, out of sight. All around —red . . . *crimson red . . . a maelstrom of black and red . . . Harry stands in a white smock as shrouded in cloud . . . he's looking at her . . . he's pinioned in the cloud . . . mid-lake, where red verges on black, the brace of swans whiten like twin statues against the dark of night, gaze at her . . . call her . . .*

She twisted and thrashed about in Fella's hands. They were standing by the half-open latrine gate. No use wasting words. The Daniella between her hands she can still handle, keep between herself and the wall. But that one blazing in Daniella's eyes—that one can't be broken, can't be held against the wall. They'll all go crazy here. What's the use? She's the one that sent her to Niederwalden. Who could have seen it coming? Tzippora Shafran's end is all set for Daniella. They'll all go crazy here. Daniella won't escape the Execution Square, as Tzippora Shafran didn't escape it.

She let her hands drop from Daniella's shoulders.

Daniella stopped writhing. She stood serene, still, looking directly at Fella's face, as though she were only just noticing her. Her hands were extended to Fella: in one hand—the notebook, in the other—the locket. Her eyes impaled Fella's.

"Get these to my brother in Niederwalden."

Fella angrily snatched the notebook and locket from the outstretched hands and ran toward the back of the latrine. She wanted to dump the things into one of the latrine holes. Daniella's mushy request sounded silly, and exasperated her. She was used to taking care of her like a mother and big sister. But as she ran to the latrine holes she couldn't shake Daniella's look from her eyes. This was a look she had never seen before—new, piercing, overpowering. A person who looks like that is way above her. She suddenly felt she couldn't dare throw the things into the holes. But she was still furious. She had to let it off somehow. She wheeled around and flung the notebook and locket deep into the block.

When she got back to the latrine gate—it was too late.

The spot where Daniella had been standing a moment ago was empty.

From out the darkness Daniella's white-draped figure moved off. She was pacing straight for the lake, moving into the reddish light of the wide camp road. The night crouching on both sides of the barbed wire opened red, inflamed eyes and tensely followed the movements of the delicate form of the girl in the white linen nightgown coming directly into its waiting maw.

Fella clung to the latrine doorpost. She was too terrified to utter a sound. Her fearful eyes strained toward the dwindling white silhouette, as though wishing to tear out after Daniella, seize her and force her back into the darkness. If only she could call out to her, warn her again! Daniella was now exposed to all the watchtowers posted along the whole length of the road. The slightest outcry—and it's all over. It's all over, anyway. There's no stopping it. No way out any more. Any second now.

From the darkness blanketing the back end of the bridge, the black figure of the SS sentry peeled out like a bared fang of the night. He aimed his gun slowly, deliberately, as though still not believing his own eyes. He isn't sure yet of the windfall that has come his way, though he clearly sees his lucky number right there in front of him. He sees the "three-day furlough" drawing near. It's in the bag. It's already out of the bailiwick of the other watchtowers. But he's careful. Stalks with bated breath, and waits.

The white silhouette fades slowly up the sloping road to the lake. She doesn't run. She doesn't turn her head. She walks proud, erect. Facing her are the brace of swans like a twin sculpture——

The night answered the gunburst with wild, rollicking laughter. The watchtowers all along the road perked up and bent an ear. The SS sentry on the bridge couldn't curb the billows of laughter rearing up in him and he sent them tumbling down to the last watchtower on the road: let all Kameraden know that next morning he gets three days' furlough. His "kill" is right here inside his territory. Ho-o-o, did he pull that off shrewd and careful. He let his "game" get near the water. Didn't shoot a second before. You've got to know how to time it right. And he knew, the bridge sentry did!

220

Up at the head of the road a splotch whitened. With an outstretched black tongue the night lapped up the spilled blood of the seventeen-year-old Doll. The twin swan statue suddenly came to life. The gunburst had frightened them out of their marble serenity, and with outspread wings they went gliding quickly away from the camp shore, as if bearing on their white wings the tortured life of Daniella Preleshnik.

Fella stood glued to the latrine wall.

From tower to tower the German voices enviously shrilled the news of the bonanza one of the `Kameraden had just come into.

From the nearby KB block the horrible cooing did not let up. The venereal girls were weeping in their isolation over the van coming for them at daybreak. The bridge sentry, intoxicated with joy, struck the pose of an opera singer on stage, and from the top of his lungs let the night air ring with the German soldier-song:

"Ha-heilee-lu-la-la . . ."

Who can come up to him? Tomorrow he's going to his family. Maybe—to mother, waiting at home. Maybe—to sister, or—to little only-daughter whom he so pines for as he stands here on the bridge. Maybe his little girl is as old as the "kill" in the white nightgown lying there on the road. Three days' furlough. Let's see you match that!

Fella couldn't bear to stand there any more. The dove-cooing from the depths of the KB block was driving her mad. She couldn't bear it any more. She went back into the latrine block.

On the ground, at the other end of the block, lay the notebook and the locket. She bent and picked them up. She felt as though Daniella's life now rested on the palms of her hands. *"Get these to my brother in Niederwalden."* She tucked the notebook into her camp smock, on her bosom. Her flesh quivered at the feel of the paper on her heart.

On high, behind and through the cloud shreds, the crescent moon hurried on. Fella couldn't bear any more to look into the night, at the splotch whitening on the road. She paced up and down the row of latrine holes bisecting the block. Strange emotions, hitherto unknown to her, fermented in her heart.

With both hands she held the locket up to her eyes. Out

of the photo Daniella gazed at her, dressed in her white sailor-collared school outfit, two thick white-ribboned braids tumbling down to her breast, her gaze serene, pure, innocent. Beside her, on a round table, sat Moni. The child looked at Fella with wide-eyed wonderment, the question seeming to hover on his lips: *Why is Dani lying on the road?*

She hugged the two children to her lips. At the moment, all feeling of hatred seemed to evaporate from her. At the moment her hatred toward the Germans swept over all the bounds of her senses. So deep was this hate, she could no longer see it. She wanted to hate, but she didn't know whom to hate.

She couldn't get herself to hate the Judenrat—they were so puny, so no-account as against the tidal waves of misery breaking around her. Nor could she hate the Germans—so trivial, so insignificant as against the remorseless, bottomless grief. Her hate was too vast, too deep for her to know at whom to hurl it. She couldn't even hate God, now.

She sat down on one of the latrine holes. The grief rocked her to and fro. Her legs were stretched out before her. She saw them as through a veil of mist. They recalled a long-ago world—gone, forgotten. Now her legs seemed superfluous. Even the long-ago world—superfluous and pointless.

She got up. Half the latrine door was open. She went toward the door. Now she can even go outside. Let them shoot her if they like. She doesn't feel the least bit afraid. Now she can stand in full view of the watchtowers. Now she can look the SS men straight in the eye. She can indifferently toss them the three-day furlough her life is still worth. Let them scramble like filthy beggars for the boon she is tossing them on the ground.

Above the tree-crests, beyond the bridge, the new day planted a foot. Soon the black van will pull up at the KB. Daniella was lying, face down, one hand slung before her on the road. *"Get these to my brother in Niederwalden."* All at once, Fella felt a light ray pierce the darkness in her mind. For the first time she felt she had something for which she was ready to give her life. She abandoned herself completely to this feeling, as a blind man reaching out to a suddenly restored light. She pressed the notebook under the camp smock to her heart. She hid back in the latrine so that no one should find her here at this hour, and waited for the first gong.

222

The day strode toward the camp. Passing over the road, it stubbed its foot against a riddled body. It glimpsed down, and went on——

HAVING COMPLETED THIS BOOK,

I cannot leave without mentioning

PROFESSOR DR. YOSEF
and
MRS. MALKA ASHERMAN
Tel Aviv

They found me when I was floundering in a sea of ashes—the ashes to which all my family and world were reduced in the crematorium of Auschwitz—and reached out devoted arms to me as parents to their child, and spared nothing to make it possible for me to go on living in this world.